Foreword

CIRIA's research programme *Methane and associated hazards to construction* provides guidance for the construction industry about landfill gases, naturally occuring methane and other gases..

In addition to a bibliography relevant to methane and construction (CIRIA Special Publication 79) and a study of the construction industry's needs for research and information on methane (CIRIA Project Report 5), the publications of the programme include guidance documents on the nature, origins and occurrence of methane (CIRIA Report 130) on its detection, measurements and monitoring (CIRIA Report 131), on the investigation of sites for methane (CIRIA Report 150), on the interpretation of subsurface gas measurements (CIRIA Report 151) and on the assessment of degrees of risk (CIRIA Report 152).

This report, dealing with the protection of new and existing developments, is the result of the fifth project in the programme. It was prepared by Dr. G. B. Card of Frank Graham Consulting Engineers Ltd under contract to CIRIA.

Following CIRIA's usual practice, the research study was guided by a Steering Group which comprised:

Mr. A. F. Johns (Chairman),	Kyle Stewart Design Services Ltd
Dr. A. J. Burke	Department of the Environment
Miss J. Denner	Department of the Environment
Dr. R. Gregory	Environmental Resources Ltd
Mr. R. Hartless	Building Research Establishment
Mr. R. W. Johnson	National House-Building Council
Mr. J. McEntee	Wimpey Environmental Ltd
Mr. D. P. McNicholl	Wardell Armstrong
Mr. A. P. Russell	Leicester City Council
Mr. P. J. Smith	Oldham Metropolitan Borough Council
Mr M. G. Staff	Wardell Armstrong
Mr. P. Willcocks	Department of the Environment

CIRIA's Research Managers for this project were Mr. F. M. Jardine and Mr. R. Freer.

Acknowledgements

The project was funded under Phase II of the programme of *Methane and associated hazards to construction* by:

Department of the Environment, Construction Directorate
Anglian Water Services Ltd
North West Water Ltd
Southern Water Services Ltd
Yorkshire Water Services Ltd
CIRIA Core Programme

CIRIA and Frank Graham Consulting Engineers Limited are grateful for help given to this project by the funders, by the members of the Steering Group and by the many individuals and organisations who were consulted. Contributions from Mr N. Gill of James Nisbet and Partners are also gratefully acknowledged.

Acknowledgement is made to the following organisations who provided and gave CIRIA permission to use illustrative material:

Box 7	Amec Civil Engineering Ltd
Box 8	Frederick Sherrell
Box 10	Director of the Technical and Development Services, Sandwell Metropolitan Borough Council
Box 25	Director of the Technical and Development Services, Sandwell Metropolitan Borough Council

Figure 14(a)	Netlon Ltd
Figure 14(b)	Gundle Lining Systems Inc
Figure 14(c)	Monarflex Geomembranes Ltd
Figure 15	Monarflex Geomembranes Ltd
Figure 17(a)	SLT Lining Technology GmbH
Figure 17(b)	Gundle Lining Systems Inc
Figure 17(c)	Aloys Guber
Figure 22	Environmental Resources Ltd
Figure 23	Borough Planning Officer, Oldham Metropolitan Borough Council
Figure 25(b)	Borough Planning Officer, Oldham Metropolitan Borough Council
Figure 27	Thomas Graveson Ltd
Figure 31	James Nisbet and Partners
Figure 32	Wimpey Environmental Ltd
Figure 33	James Nisbet and Partners
Figure 36	Aspinwall and Company Ltd
Figure 38	Aspinwall and Company Ltd
Figure 40	Aspinwall and Company Ltd
Figure 41	Colas Building Products Ltd
Figure 42	Monarflex Geomembranes Ltd
Figure 43(b)	Cremer and Warner
Figure 45	Sabre Gas Detection Ltd
Figure 47(b)	Gundle Lining Systems Inc
Figure 48	James Nisbet and Partners
Figure 49	Kyle Stewart Design Services Ltd
Figure 50	Colas Building Products Ltd
Figure 51	Monarflex Geomembranes Ltd
Figure 52	Colas Building Products Ltd

Contents

Figures 7

Boxes 8

Tables 9

Glossary 11

Notation 13

Abbreviations 14

1   INTRODUCTION 17
    1.1 Scope and objectives 18
    1.2 Method 18
    1.3 The layout of the report 19

2   NEED FOR PROTECTION 21
    2.1 Occurrence 21
    2.2 Migration mechanisms and pathways 27
         2.2.1 Gaseous phase 27
         2.2.2 Gas in solution 29
    2.3 Entry routes into buildings and services 31
    2.4 Behaviour of gas in buildings 33
         2.4.1 Instantaneous mixing 34
         2.4.2 Gas layering 35
    2.5 Hazards and design criteria 35
         2.5.1 Flammability and explosivity 36
         2.5.2 Physiological effects 37
         2.5.3 Odour 37
         2.5.4 Effects on vegetation 38
         2.5.5 Design criteria 38

3   PRINCIPLES OF PROTECTION 40
    3.1 Suitability of development 41
    3.2 Conceptual design 42
    3.3 Available protection techniques 45
         3.3.1 Removal of source 45
         3.3.2 Barriers 46
         3.3.3 Dilution and dispersion 46
         3.3.4 Gas monitoring and alarms 49
         3.3.5 Miscellaneous techniques 49
    3.4 Difference of approach for new and existing development 50

4   BASIC REQUIREMENTS FOR GAS PROTECTION 52
    4.1 Design and construction of ground slabs 52
    4.2 Excavation and disposal 55

5   IN-GROUND BARRIERS 57
    5.1 Definition and application 57
    5.2 Principal types of barriers 58
    5.3 Requirements and material selection 59

5.4 Natural soil barriers 62
    5.4.1 Clay 62
    5.4.2 Soil/bentonite mixtures 65
5.5 Synthetic barriers 67
    5.5.1 Material properties 66
    5.5.2 Methods of installation 70
5.6 Bentonite slurry admixtures 74
    5.6.1 Principles of design 74
    5.6.2 Types of slurry trench cut-off barriers 76
5.7 Barriers formed by grouting techniques 78
5.8 Barriers formed by piling techniques 81

6   IN-GROUND VENTING 83
6.1 Passive in-ground venting 83
    6.1.1 Principles of design 83
    6.1.1 Methods of installation and applications 84
6.2 Active in-ground abstraction 90
    6.2.1 Principles of design 91
    6.2.2 Installation components 91
    6.2.3 Applications 93

7   VENTING FOR BUILDINGS 98
7.1 Passive venting for buildings 98
    7.1.1 Principles of design 99
    7.1.2 Methods of installation 104
    7.1.3 Applications 107
7.2 Active venting for buildings 108
    7.2.1 Principles of design 110
    7.2.2 Applications 115

8   MEMBRANES 118
8.1 Principles of design and installation 118
    8.1.1 Membranes at formation level 120
    8.1.2 In-structure membranes 122
8.2 Applications 127

9   GAS MONITORING AND ALARMS 128
9.1 Gas monitoring equipment 129
9.2 Applications 133
    9.2.1 In-ground gas monitoring 135

10 GAS-CONTROL SYSTEMS 141
    10.1   Systems used for methane and carbon dioxide 141
    10.2   Current gas control practice 143

11 PROTECTION TO EXISTING DEVELOPMENT 146
    11.1   In-ground protection measures 146
    11.2   Protection measures to buildings 149
    11.3   Effect of building modifications 152

12 SERVICES AND SUBSTRUCTURES 156
    12.1   In ground protection to services 156
    12.2   Protection at service entry points 158

12.3   Protection to subsurface developments.. 162
        12.3.1   In-ground barriers 164
        12.3.2   In-ground venting 165
        12.3.3   Internal venting to substructures 167

13   LONG-TERM MANAGEMENT 171

14   CURRENT CAPABILITIES.. 175

REFERENCES 178

Figures

Figure 1   Report structure.. 20
Figure 2   Potential for methane migration in longwall mining 28
Figure 3   Gas entry routes into buildings 32
Figure 4   Buoyancy of methane/carbon dioxide mixtures relative to air 34
Figure 5   Available gas protection techniques 40
Figure 6   Flow chart for development suitability 41
Figure 7   Principle of gas dispersion from the ground surface.................... 48
Figure 8   Typical raft construction 53
Figure 9   Principle of modified concrete raft used for gas protection.......... 54
Figure 10   Principal types of in-ground barrier.. 58
Figure 11   Principal uses of vertical barriers.. 60
Figure 12   Relationship between clay compaction and permeability 64
Figure 13   Use of synthetic barriers 66
Figure 14   Typical details of some composite synthetic barriers 67
Figure 15   In-ground synthetic barrier placed in open trench 70
Figure 16   Installation of synthetic barrier in trench excavation................... 72
Figure 17   Types of interlock system used for synthetic barriers.................. 73
Figure 18   Typical installation for bentonite: cement in-ground barrier
                incorporating a synthetic liner 76
Figure 19   Principle of jet grouting to form in-ground barrier 79
Figure 20   Vibrated beam in-ground barrier 81
Figure 21   Installation sequence for secant pile cut-off barrier 82
Figure 22   Examples of venting trenches.. 86
Figure 23   General arrangement of venting manhole...................................... 87
Figure 24   Applications of gas venting wells 88
Figure 25   Use of gas drainage layers 89
Figure 26   General arrangement of gas abstraction well 94
Figure 27   Example of portable active abstraction and flaring plant 96
Figure 28   Gas contaminant entering a ventilated space 99
Figure 29   Principle of passive venting beneath a building........................... 100
Figure 30   Methods of increasing passive venting to an underslab void.................. 102
Figure 31   Venting arrangements for underslab void...................................... 103
Figure 32   External ventilation installed in walls and beneath steps.......... 105

Figure 33 Venting arrangements for granular filled void.. 106

Figure 34 Examples of pipework arrangement in underfloor void 109

Figure 35 Principal types of active venting systems 111

Figure 36 General arrangement of active venting system to underslab void 113

Figure 37 Venting requirements in combined passive and active systems 116

Figure 38 Vent stack to actively vented retail development 117

Figure 39 Principal types of membrane 120

Figure 40 Placement of membrane at foundation interface....................................... 123

Figure 41 Typical preformed membrane sections.. 124

Figure 42 Use of in-structure membranes 125

Figure 43 Typical arrangements for gas monitoring points 134

Figure 44 Layout arrangements for in-ground gas monitoring systems 136

Figure 45 Example of installed gas monitoring system within a building 138

Figure 46 Distribution of wind pressures from adjacent buildings 154

Figure 47 In-ground gas protection to services.. 157

Figure 48 Typical gas protection measures to service entry points........................... 159

Figure 49 Ventilated external service entry points.. 160

Figure 50 Preformed membrane sections for service entry points 160

Figure 51 Drainage pipework sealed to membrane... 161

Figure 52 Example of where grouping of services can cause difficulties in
sealing membrane across ground slab... 161

Figure 53 Example of active venting to substructure duct seal................................. 162

Figure 54 Principle of in-ground barriers to protect subsurface development........... 164

Figure 55 Example of gas protection to shallow depth subsurface development 166

Figure 56 Examples of gas protection measures to deep subsurface development.... 167

Figure 57 Use of active in-ground measures to protect subsurface development...... 169

Figure 58 Principle of passive venting to substructures partly below ground 170

Figure 59 A flow chart for long-term management of gas-control systems............... 171

Boxes

Box 1 Development affected by methane from decaying peat and
organic matter 25

Box 2 Examples of conceptual design for new development................................ 44

Box 3 Example of raft construction on gassing ground 54

Box 4 On-site excavation and reburial for development...................................... 56

Box 5 Use of vertical in-ground clay barrier.. 63

Box 6 Use of horizontal in-ground clay barrier.. 63

Box 7 Installation of synthetic barrier in a bentonite/cement slurry trench
cut-off 71

Box 8 Testing of a synthetic barrier in a slurry trench 72

Box 9 Grout injection of old mine workings.. 79

Box 10 Grout injection to extend depth of in-ground clay.................................... 80

Box 11 Active abstraction for protection to new development.............................. 93

Box 12   Active abstraction for protection to existing development 95

Box 13   Passive venting to residential development adjacent to landfill 107

Box 14   Passive venting using granular filled void 108

Box 15   Passive venting applied to residential development 108

Box 16   Active venting to underslab void 114

Box 17   Active venting to granular filled void 115

Box 18   Installation of a membrane within a ground slab 126

Box 19   Control of active venting system 134

Box 20   Monitoring of passive venting system 135

Box 21   Monitoring of passive venting to existing residential development 139

Box 22   Example of gas-control system 142

Box 23   Example of gas protection by excavation and disposal 147

Box 24   Protection to existing development using in-ground techniques:
case study 1 147

Box 25   Protection to existing development using in-ground techniques:
case study 2 148

Box 26   Passive venting beneath existing buildings 151

Box 27   Protection to existing industrial and leisure development 152

Box 28   Gas protection measures affected by building modifications 153

Box 29   Existing housing affected by building extension 155

Box 30   Warehouse development affected by change of use 155

Box 31   Examples of in-ground active abstraction and active venting to
subsurface development 168

Box 32   Example of long-term management strategy 172

Box 33   Example of long-term management for residential development 173

Tables

Table 1   Extent of UK consultation for this project 19

Table 2   Typical compositions of methane-containing gases 22

Table 3   Landfill gas composition 23

Table 4   Solubility of methane and associated gases in water 29

Table 5   Methane concentrations in some UK groundwaters 30

Table 6   Hazard concentrations of methane and associated gases 36

Table 7   Effects of reduced oxygen concentration 37

Table 8   Design criteria for methane gas protection measures 39

Table 9   Basic considerations for gas protection of buildings 43

Table 10   Equivalent barrier thickness for given relative permeability 46

Table 11   Differences in approach between new and existing development 51

Table 12   Various methods and materials used to form in-ground barriers for
gas protection 57

Table 13   Advantages and disadvantages of clay in-ground barriers 64

Table 14   Advantages and disadvantages of soil/bentonite for in-ground barriers 65

Table 15   Materials used for synthetic in-ground barriers 68

Table 16   Suitability of high and low density polyethylene in-ground barriers 69

Table 17 Advantages and disadvantages of passive in-ground venting.......................... 84

Table 18 Advantages and disadvantages of active in-ground abstraction 97

Table 19 Advantages and disadvantages of a granular filled void............................ 105

Table 20 Summary of typical materials used for membranes in the UK 119

Table 21 Advantages and disadvantages of membranes at formation level 121

Table 22 Gas monitoring requirements during development.................................... 128

Table 23 Typical applications of available gas monitoring instruments................... 130

Table 24 Advantages and disadvantages of instruments based on
infra-red absorption 131

Table 25 Advantages and disadvantages of instruments based on
catalytic oxidation... 132

Table 26 Advantages and limitations of instruments based on
thermal conductivity 133

Table 27 Gas-control systems to buildings for methane 143

Table 28 Gassing parameters used to characterise case study situation.................... 144

Table 29 Gas-control systems for new development: current UK practice 144

Table 30 Gas-control systems for existing development: current UK practice 145

Table 31 Summary of current capabillities.. 177

Glossary

absorption	Penetration of a substance into the body of another
aerobic	Pertaining to conditions where free oxygen is present
anaerobic	Pertaining to conditions where there is no free oxygen
asphyxiant	A vapour or gas which causes unconsciousness or death by suffocation (lack of oxygen)
biodegradation	The decomposition by bacteria
biogenic methane	Methane produced by the action of living organisms
combustion	A chemical process of oxidation that occurs at a rate fast enough to produce heat and usually light, in the form of either a glow or flames
confined space	A space having poor natural ventilation, i.e. trench, chamber or sewer, in which there is potential for hazardous concentrations of gas to accumulate
deflagration	The propagation of a combustion zone at a velocity that is greater than the speed of sound in the unreacted medium
development	Works of construction which may be buildings or civil engineering structures above or below ground and including ancillary works, installations and open spaces associated with the structures
dust	Finely divided solid particles that could be hazardous on inhalation, or constitute a fire hazard (air suspensions of particles generally less than 10 microns in diameter)
explosion	The bursting or rupture of an enclosure or a container due to the development of internal pressure from deflagration
fermentation	The breakdown of organic sugars by bacteria to produce alcohols
gas	One of the three states of matter, characterised by very low density and viscosity (relative to liquids and solids), with complete molecular mobility and indefinite expansion to occupy with almost complete uniformity the whole of any container
gas emission rate	The volume flow rate of gas from a boundary surface
gas generation rate	The volume flow rate of gas produced at source
hazard	An event, situation or condition which if it occurred could endanger life or property
landfill gas	Variable mixture of gases generated by decaying organic matter. Principal components are methane and carbon dioxide. Other constituents may include hydrogen sulphide, water vapour and other hydrocarbons
mercaptans	Organic compounds containing a sulphydryl (or thiol) group directly united to a carbon atom. They are liquids with strong unpleasant odours
mole	The quantity of a substance which contains one gram formula weight of the substance

permeability	The rate of movement of a liquid or gas under pressure through the void space in a solid media
prefabricated vertical drains	Vertical drain installed into the ground comprising a central core for fluid or gas transport surrounded by an outer covering which serves as a filter
risk	The qualitative or quantitative probability of a hazard being realised
scrim	Open weave fabric for reinforcing/lining membranes
seatearth	The fossil soils associated with a coal seam
site	The land on or in which the development is or will be
syneresis	The separation of a liquid from a gel on standing
thermogenic methane	Methane produced by thermal degradation of organic compounds

Notation

A surface area

c gas concentration

c_a gas concentration in atmosphere

c_e equilibrium design gas concentration

$D*$ diffusion coefficient

g acceleration due to gravity

i pressure gradient

K effective permeability of ground to gas

K_b Henry's Law constant

L layering number

p_b partial pressure of the gas

P_a atmospheric pressure

P_o pressure of gas at source

q volume flow rate of gas ingress

Q volume flow rate of fresh air

t time

U ventilation velocity

W width of gas-forming layer

x_b mole fraction of solute

X distance in x-direction from surface boundary

ρ_a relative density of air

ρ_g relative density of gas

Abbreviations

atm	atmosphere(s)
BASEEFA	British Approval Service for Electrical Equipment in Flammable Atmospheres
BS	British Standard
BSI	British Standard Institution
BRE	Building Research Establishment
CENELEC	European Committee for Electrotechnical Standardisation
CIBSE	Chartered Institution of Building Service Engineers
CMHC	Canada Mortgage and Housing Corporation
CSS	County Surveyors' Society
DIAL	Differential absorption laser detection systems
DoE	Department of the Environment
DTp	Department of Transport
dpm	damp-proof membrane
dpc	damp-proof course
EPA	Environmental Protection Agency (United States of America)
ERU	Environmental Research Unit (Republic of Ireland)
FML	Flexible membrane liners
HMIP	Her Majesty's Inspectorate of Pollution
HDPE	High density polyethylene
HSE	Health and Safety Executive
ICRCL	Interdepartmental Committee for the Redevelopment of Contaminated Land
lfg	Landfill gas
LDPE	Low density polyethylene
LEL	Lower explosive limit
LIDAR	Laser detection systems
MDPE	Medium density polyethylene
NCB	National Coal Board
NCE	New Civil Engineer
NFPA	National Fire Protection Association
NHBC	National House-Building Council
NJUG	National Joint Utilities Group

NRA	National Rivers Authority
NWWDO	North West Waste Disposal Officers
pfa	pulverised fuel ash
ppm	parts per million
PSA	Property Services Agency
PVC	Polyvinyl chloride
TRRL	Transport and Road Research Laboratory
uPVC	Unplasticised polyvinyl chloride
UEL	Upper explosive limit
VOCs	Volatile organic compounds
WAA	Water Authorities Association
WRc	Water Research Council

1 Introduction

This research report is part of the second phase of CIRIA's Environmental Geotechnics programme: *Methane and associated hazards to construction.*

The first phase of the CIRIA programme comprised four research projects which resulted in the following publications:

- A bibliography of some 500 references relating to the occurrence of methane at construction sites (Hartless, 1992).

- A guidance document on the nature, origins and occurrence of methane (Hooker and Bannon, 1993).

- A guidance document on the methods of detection, sampling, measurement and monitoring of methane (Crowhurst and Manchester, 1993).

- A study to establish the priorities for research and information needed by the construction industry in relation to methane hazards (Staff and Sceal, 1992).

The second phase of the methane programme comprised two research projects that resulted in two guidance documents:

- Protection of new and existing development from methane and associated gases in the ground (this report)

- Procedures for the investigation of sites for methane and associated gases in the ground (Raybould *et al.*, 1995).

The two research projects in the final phase of CIRIA's programme are:

- The interpretation of subsurface gas concentrations (Harries *et al.*, 1995).

- Risk assessment for methane and other gases from the ground (O'Riordan and Milloy, 1995).

The widespread occurrence of methane and its ability to migrate considerable distances through the ground mean that new and existing development can be affected. Those with responsibility for existing developments, which are known to be on or close to methane-gassing ground, should consider if any changes, whether external to the site or within the site, could create additional risk.

In recent years, with many developments being constructed on and near sources of methane and with the increased awareness of the potential for hazard, various techniques have been used to protect against methane. Necessarily, the designs are often specific to the individual development or a component part. Few of the adopted solutions have been described in construction literature. Far less, is there positive confirmation of their efficacy. General principles for gas protection measures, however, are becoming established largely through the influence of the more experienced engineers and scientists. It is appropriate, therefore, to set out these general principles in a report which can be used readily by construction professionals involved with both new and existing development.

1.1 SCOPE AND OBJECTIVES

This report provides a practical guide to current accepted good practice on the selection, design and performance of methane protection measures for new and existing building development including associated works. Civil engineering development, e.g. tunnels, harbour or river works, or aspects of mining engineering are not included in the report except insofar as they may affect building development or be relevant to case examples, e.g. sewer tunnels or sites in mining areas. The comments made in the report are based on information gathered from various sources. The majority of information is from consultations with experts, practitioners, clients and owners of development, public utility engineers and those with a statutory or regulatory responsibility for development.

In addition, findings of the previous research undertaken as part of the CIRIA Environmental Geotechnics programme: *Methane and associated hazards to construction* have also been used (Hartless, 1992; Hooker and Bannon, 1993 and Crowhurst and Manchester, 1993).

The report describes the hazards and perceived risks to development, the need for gas protection and the various techniques and measures which have been adopted. Review and analysis of this information has allowed broad conclusions to be drawn regarding the efficacy of protection measures, their suitability to new or existing development, reliability and performance. In addition, the findings of the report have allowed identification of aspects where further research and work to improve the methods of design and efficacy of protection measures could be made.

The results and findings of the project and the present state of knowledge are such that it is not possible to lay down rigid design rules, but only to present guidelines on general principles and best available practice for the design and installation of gas protection measures to development. Further research and long-term monitoring of performance of constructed gas-protection measures are required in order to be able to provide guidance regarding design, reliability and efficacy.

Semi-quantitative design principles are available for certain elements of gas protection, e.g. active abstraction, passive venting and passive or active venting for buildings. However, these design principles have limited application in the context of the overall building/development where other parameters and variables must be taken into account. These include:

- ease of construction and installation
- durability and serviceability
- the layout and use of the development together with allowance for future changes in use or occupancy.

Safe working practices on or adjacent to gassing land during investigation and construction of development are not covered by this Report. Guidance on this subject is given by Barry *et al.* (1992) and HSE (1991).

1.2 METHOD

To establish the methods and practices used for gas protection measures to development, information was gathered from a number of sources as follows:

- a literature review of published information both in the UK and overseas

- consultation with individuals and organisations involved in development affected by gassing ground
- consultation and correspondence with specialist manufacturers of products used for gas protection
- information and guidance received from the Project Steering Group
- experience of the Research Contractor.

CIRIA Special Publication 79 (Hartless, 1992) was used as the primary reference source of published information. From this document more than 100 case-study references were obtained and reviewed. This was supplemented by information from more recent publications and unpublished works.

Consultations were made with 85 organisations in the UK, who were identified as having specific knowledge or experience of development on land effected by gas. Table 1 summarises the organisations contacted.

Initially organisations were contacted by letter and provided with an outline of the objectives of the project and invited to contribute by providing any relevant information regarding protection of new or existing development from methane and associated gases. A high level of response was received from a large proportion of those organisations contacted. Further discussions together with detailed examination of case studies were conducted with some 35 individual consultees within these organisations.

Table 1 Extent of UK consultation for this project

Type of organisation	Number contacted	Total number of consultees
Central government and research institutes	6	12
Builders/developers	11	13
Consultant engineers	8	13
Environmental consultants	8	11
Local authorities and development corporations	34	45
Owners/occupiers	4	9
Product manufacturers	9	11
Utility organisations	5	7

In addition to contributions from the UK, information from overseas practitioners and organisations was also sought. A significant amount of information comprising current design practices and documented case studies was gathered *via* the International Council for Building Research and Documentation: Task Group 1 – Contaminated Land. This included contributions from Algeria, Canada, USA, Ireland, Finland and Germany. Additional information on overseas experience was also gathered from Hong Kong and Indonesia.

1.3 THE LAYOUT OF THE REPORT

Figure 1 introduces the main layout and structure of the report. The text is structured to follow a logical sequence in development planning and construction commencing with identification and assessment of the problems and hazards from methane and associated gases to installation of appropriate gas protection measures and finally monitoring and long-term management of gas control systems. This structure is repeated for existing development and services and substructures which are discussed in separate sections.

The report has been structured so that each section may be read as a whole, independent of other parts of the text. Where appropriate, however, cross-references to other sections of the text have been included where further relevant or useful information may be found. In addition, aspects of the previous CIRIA research projects (Hooker and Bannon, 1993 and Crowhurst and Manchester, 1993) have been summarised and incorporated in order to place sections of the report in context. Examples and case studies of the methods and practices used for gas protection to development are incorporated in boxes and supplement the main body of the text. In a number of instances case studies are accompanied by figures.

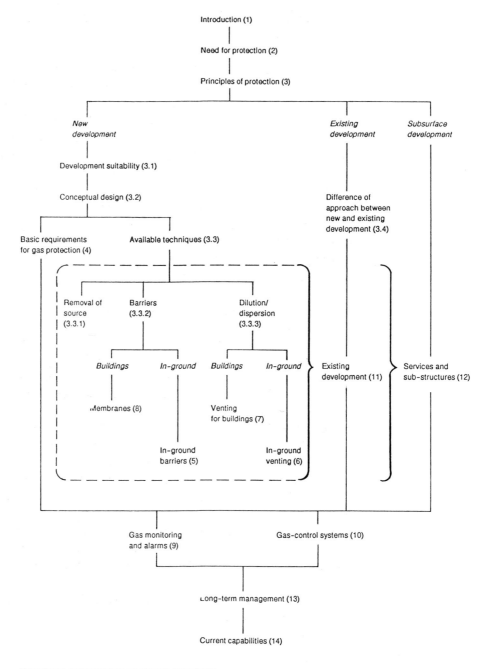

Note : Report section numbers are shown in parentheses

Figure 1 Report structure

2   Need for protection

2.1   OCCURRENCE

Methane is the most abundant organic chemical in the Earth's atmosphere. It is formed under anaerobic conditions by the chemical reduction of organic matter by micro-organisms (biogenic methane), or biologically over geological periods of time following burial, compression and heating of organic material (thermogenic methane). Methane can be found in many different environments and soil/rock strata together with associated gases. Hooker and Bannon (1993) provide technical guidance on the nature and occurrence of methane and associated gases together with their hazards.

Building development is usually founded on soils or rocks at shallow depth beneath the ground surface. In most situations, near-surface soils will tend to be low in organic content and have very low potential for methane generation. Typically the methane concentration in most UK soils falls well below 0.1% by volume in air with negligible rates of surface emission. In these circumstances the gas is adequately diluted and dispersed on release into the atmosphere at ground surface. The average concentration of methane in the atmosphere is 1.65 ppm although this is increasing at an appreciable rate because of environmental effects such as global warming (Harrison, 1990). Normal construction practice is to remove topsoil and near-surface soils containing roots and vegetation which may produce methane and associated gases as a result of biodegradation of organic matter from beneath the building development. Guidance is given in the Building Regulations Approved Document, Part C, Section 1 (DoE, 1992) regarding site preparation and removal of organic matter.

However, soils/rocks high in organic content can occur and may produce high levels of methane and associated gases. High concentrations of carbon dioxide can also be produced by these and other natural processes including aerobic decomposition of organic matter and acidic groundwater reacting with carbonate rocks, e.g. chalk and carboniferous limestone. Gas migration from these soils/rocks or exposure of the sources themselves because of construction activities can result in the release of unacceptable volumes of gas which can affect development. Approved Document, Part C2 of The Building Regulations (DoE, 1992) gives guidance for methane and carbon dioxide concentrations in the ground. In broad terms, gas protection measures are considered necessary where the concentrations of methane and/or carbon dioxide exceed 1% and 1.5% by volume in air respectively. In the specific case of development near to landfill sites Waste Management Paper 27 (DoE, 1991) recommends that the local waste disposal authority should be consulted regarding any proposed development less than 250 m from the boundary of a site which has received waste in the previous 30 years. This boundary limit has been incorporated into Planning Circular 17/89 (DoE, 1989a) and the General Development Order 1988 has been amended to include it.

The main sources of methane and associated gases that may be encountered during building development are:

- landfills
- mine workings
- wetlands
- sewers

- gas mains
- miscellaneous sources.

Typical compositions of methane containing gases from these various sources likely to be encountered during building development are given in Table 2. It should be appreciated, however, that the composition of any gas is not constant and can change both with time and distance of migration from source. In aerobic conditions methane can be oxidised to carbon dioxide and water, while in anaerobic conditions carbon dioxide can be reduced to methane. Gas molecules can also be absorbed on to soil particles through which they pass separating the gas mixture into its components in a similar manner to the principle of gas chromatography.

Table 2 Typical compositions of methane-containing gases

Source	Gas composition % by volume in air							
	CH_4	C_2H_6	C_3H_8	CO_2	CO	H_2S	N_2	O_2
Landfill gas [1]	20–65			16–57	$<1 \times 10^{-4}$	2×10^{-5}	0.5–37	<0.3
Mine gas								
seam	80–95	8	4	0.2–6			2–9	
pumped drainage [2]	22–95	3	1	0.5–6	0-10		1–61	
Wetlands/peat lands								
freshwater muds [3]	3–86			0.3–13			16–94	
saltwater muds	55–79			2–13				
marsh gas	11–88						3–69	
buried peats and organic soils	45–97						1.6–54	
Mains/natural gas [4]	94	3.2	0.6	0.5			1.2	

Notes:
1. See also Table 3.
2. Gas mixed with air.
3. Composition varies with depth.
4. Also 0.2% C_4H_{10} (butane).

The various sources of methane and associated gases are discussed below:

Landfills

Landfill gas (lfg) is one of the products of fermentation and biodegradation of organic material contained in various municipal, commercial and industrial wastes disposed in landfill sites. It can also be produced from certain 'inert' fills such as ash and foundry sands. Landfill gas is principally a mixture of methane and carbon dioxide, although it also includes a large number of minor gaseous components. The rate of generation of individual gases and hence composition will vary widely depending on the age and state of biodegradation. This can be because of waste type, depth of deposit, effects of atmospheric pressure, temperature and rainfall, pH value and moisture content of the waste. Table 3 lists the typical composition of landfill gas observed in the UK. Waste Management Paper 27 (DoE, 1991) and ICRCL Guidance Note 17/78 (1990) give a useful description of landfill gas production and its variability.

Table 3   Landfill gas composition (from Waste Management Paper No 27: DoE, 1991)

Component	Typical value (% volume in air)	Observed maximum (% volume in air)
Methane	66.8[1]	88.0[2]
Carbon dioxide	33.6[1]	89.3[1]
Oxygen	0.16[1]	20.9[1,3]
Nitrogen	2.4[1]	87.0[2,3]
Hydrogen	0.05[4]	21.1[1]
Carbon monoxide	0.001[4]	0.09[2]
Ethane	0.005[4]	0.0139[2]
Ethene	0.018[4]	–
Acetaldehyde	0.005[4]	–
Propane	0.002[4]	0.0171[2]
Butanes	0.003[4]	0.023[1]
Helium	0.00005	–
Higher alkanes	<0.05[2]	0.07[1]
Unsaturated hydrocarbons	0.009[1]	0.048[1]
Halogenated compounds	0.00002[1]	0.032[1]
Hydrogen sulphide	0.00002[1]	35.0[1]
Organosulphur compounds	0.00001[1]	0.028[1]
Alcohols	0.00001[1]	0.127[1]
Others	0.00005[1]	0.023[1]

Notes:

1. Data taken from Waste Management Paper 26 (DoE,1986).

2. Published data supplied by Aspinwall & Company Ltd.

3. Entirely derived from the atmosphere.

4. Taken from: Guilani, A. J. 'Application of conventional oil and gas drilling techniques to the production of gas from garbage', American Gas Association Transmission Conference, Salt Lake City, Utah, 5–7 May 1980.

5. Landfill gas is usually saturated with water vapour, up to 4% by weight depending on the gas temperature. At 25°C a value of 1.8% by weight is typical.

6. When undertaking initial confirmatory analysis by gas chromatography, the first five compounds listed above are usually identified when looking for the presence of landfill gas.

In December 1987, Her Majesty's Inspectorate of Pollution (HMIP) wrote to all Waste Disposal Authorities (WDAs) in England and Wales asking them to:

*   review existing disposal licences to ensure that appropriate measures to control landfill gas were specified

*   list active landfills and those closed in the previous 10 years that were generating landfill gas and estimate the quantities involved

*   indicate which sites were close to housing

*   indicate which closed sites had been subject to any redevelopment

*   describe the measures taken to control gas.

The results of this survey suggested that there were about 1400 active and closed sites which could be sources of landfill gas problems, about half of them were within 250 m of housing or industry (HMIP, 1991). Subsequent to this survey, guidance to local planning authorities and developers regarding development control on landfill sites and nearby land was issued in DoE Circular 17/89 (DoE, 1989a). This circular sought to ensure that planning decisions were taken which took account of the risk to development from the migration of landfill gas. Incidents have been recorded where landfill gas has affected development located up to 1 km from the source (Johnson, 1986).

Mine workings

The most common gas encountered in mines and mining areas is methane (fire damp). Geological methane is usually associated with coal-bearing carboniferous strata and is produced by the anaerobic decomposition of ancient vegetation trapped within the rock. Higher alkanes (such as ethane), hydrogen and helium may also be present. Carbon dioxide (black damp) may also be present in coal mine workings resulting from oxidation of methane. There is also evidence of carbon dioxide and possibly nitrogen originating from old ironstone mines. The latter is believed to be caused by the absorption of oxygen by iron-bearing rocks (pyrite, haematite, etc.) during oxidation leading to nitrogen-rich atmospheres.

Methane encountered during mining operations can originate from a number of sources (Creedy, 1989). These are:

- as a free gas within the coal seam being worked on

- absorbed on the surface of fissures and pores in the seam

- absorbed within the internal structure of the coal

- from non-coal strata such as shale, sandstone, seatearth or colliery spoil

- dissolved groundwater at very high pressures within the carboniferous rocks which is released from solution when the pressure is reduced to atmospheric in the mine.

Unworked seams surrounding the seam being worked can also produce methane. Natural degassing of coal measures may occur at ground surface or at depth. In the Wigan area incidents of burning wells and explosions which destroyed housing were reported well before the Wigan coal field was developed (Robinson and Grayson, 1990, and Williams and Hitchman, 1989). Development of the mines including methane drainage and subsurface venting reduced surface emission of methane and the incidents of explosions. Abandoned mines can be the source of surface gas emissions because of recent closure of an adjacent connected mine. Termination of mine drainage can result in the increase in groundwater levels and flooding of underground workings. This in turn can result in quick release or expulsion of methane from the workings at ground surface because of the pumping or piston effect of a rising groundwater table describes several case studies in Northern England where existing development has been affected by mine gas from old mine workings.

Wetlands

Areas such as marshes, peatlands, lakes and estuaries are all potential sources of methane together with carbon dioxide and hydrogen sulphide. Releases of methane from wetland environments into the atmosphere are considered to be the largest natural source of methane (Quay *et al.,* 1988). Methane from wetlands is formed by the microbial decay of organic material under anaerobic conditions, usually waterlogged vegetation. A proportion of the methane that is produced in marshy or peaty environments is oxidised to carbon dioxide. In a study of the composition of gases from freshwater and brackish water environments, Swain (1986) found concentrations of methane, up to 50% to 90% by volume in air, carbon dioxide up to 4% to 15% by volume in air, and small or trace amounts of hydrogen, carbon monoxide, hydrogen sulphide and light hydrocarbons.

In general the geographical location of wetland environments, soft compressible ground conditions and high water table will naturally limit development in these areas. However, with increasing demands for building land, partial development of these areas may occur in conjunction with land, reclamation and drainage, giving rise to a potential source of methane affecting existing development. In the UK development has occurred on former wetland areas, e.g. Somerset, South Wales and the Fenlands in Norfolk, without any apparent incident or problem from methane and associated gases. This may be for two reasons:

1. Although high gas concentrations may be encountered on initial exposure the rate of gas generation is low and is rapidly diluted and dispersed into the atmosphere leaving very low background levels.

2. In the majority of cases where development has occurred a relatively low-permeability stratum, e.g. clay or clayey silt (i.e. an alluvial deposit) overlies the gas-producing zone and acts as a horizontal barrier preventing, or significantly reducing, vertical gas migration. Any surface emission of gas that occurs is rapidly diluted and dispersed into the atmosphere. On reclaimed wetlands in south Wales methane concentrations of up to 25% by volume in air have been recorded in buried peat deposits with rates of generation equivalent to $1 \times 10^{-3}\,m^3/min$. No incident of gas ingress has been identified new or existing development. Nevertheless, incidents can occur as demonstrated by the case study outlined in Box 1.

Box 1   Development affected by methane from decaying peat and organic matter

The Canada Mortgage and Housing Corporation undertook a comprehensive study to evaluate the extent of soil gas infiltration into development in Canada (Fugler, 1992). This study identified more than 100 cases of existing residential and commercial development affected by methane and associated gases including volatile organic compounds (VOCs). In some 10% of these cases the source of methane was identified as decaying peat or organic matter. In several, methane concentrations in excess of 40% by volume in air were detected within the soils surrounding existing development and in some instances methane concentrations ranging from 2% to 18% by volume in air were recorded directly beneath buildings. Gas protection measures adopted ranged from retro-fitting existing buildings with underslab active venting systems (see Section 7.2) to the use of membranes laid at formation level beneath new buildings (see Section 8.2). In all cases where gas protection measures have been installed long-term monitoring (up to three years in some cases) has not revealed any problems with methane ingress into buildings or structures.

Sewers

The main components of gas originating from sewers are methane and carbon dioxide but hydrogen sulphide may also be present. The process of formation is anaerobic decomposition of the organic putrescible components of sewage. Sewer gas is a problem in sewerage systems including pipework, manholes and service chambers, pump stations and plant rooms because of limited ventilation which can lead to potentially explosive or asphyxiant or toxic atmospheres. Corrosion of concrete pipes can occur also because of the formation of sulphuric acid from the oxidation of hydrogen sulphide. This can lead to structural failure of pipes or pipe joints which in turn can result in migration of sewer gas into adjacent ground and/or development.

Mains gas

Mains (natural) gas is predominantly methane (with an added stenching agent) and has the same geological source as methane in coal mines. Leaks of mains gas can occur from fractured underground pipes. This in turn can lead to gas migration into surrounding ground and/or development, or within the granular permeable backfill of the gas pipeline or other utilities. Clow (1991) discusses a number of incidents where gas explosions in telecommunication buildings, chambers and ducts were found to be due to leaking mains gas. During migration of piped gas a small proportion of methane may be oxidised to carbon dioxide.

Miscellaneous sources

There are many miscellaneous sources in the ground of methane and associated gases which may affect development. These include:

- compost heaps
- fly tipping of biodegradable wastes
- cemeteries
- buried farm animal carcasses
- farm-yard dung heaps
- old cess pits.

In the majority of these situations the gassing source is localised, of limited extent and isolated. While initial gas concentrations may be high the actual total volume of gas is usually small and will have limited influence on development. It is only in situations where building development is located directly over the gassing source that a risk may exist. In all situations where a potential gassing source is identified, gas monitoring and evaluation will be required to assess the need for gas protection.

Other man-made sources include certain types of building materials which can be degraded by microbes, or in some other way, to produce methane. Building materials such as timber, cardboard and paper are composed of organic material (cellulose) and under anaerobic conditions may be degraded to produce methane and carbon dioxide. Void formers made from these materials which have been widely used under ground beams and slabs to reduce the effects of clay heave have been known to produce methane and carbon dioxide in the anaerobic conditions created at the ground/foundation interface. During 1990 there were reports that void formers used in the foundation construction of buildings on clay sites were a source of methane generation. In one incident an ignition source caused a minor explosion in a basement in London. Such cases have resulted in the introduction of modified void formers manufactured with a high percentage of inert non-degradable material such as polystyrene, polypropylene and calcium silicate. The potential volume of gas generated from void formers made from these materials is considerably reduced.

Certain waste materials used as construction fill can also be a source of gas. Foundry sands can contain organic materials resulting from the foundry process such a phenolic binders, dextrin and coal dust. They will often contain other general foundry wastes of a potentially gas-generating nature such as wood, rags and paper. They can provide a substrate for methanogenic bacteria because of the presence of carbon-rich nutrient in addition to the large surface area offered by the sand grains. Foundry sands are encountered both as a constituent of mixed fills and as screened and sorted engineered fill. Where unscreened and deposited as a waste, foundry sands have been shown to generate methane at concentrations of up to 50% by volume in air but, as the corresponding generation rates tend to be low, the actual volume of gas emitted is small. Gas generation rates within screened and compacted foundry sands are usually extremely low. As with any potential source of methane and associated gases, monitoring and evaluation of the gassing regime should be undertaken to assess the need and scope of protection measures.

2.2 MIGRATION MECHANISMS AND PATHWAYS

Within the ground, methane and associated gases may exist in either a gaseous phase or dissolved within the groundwater. In either phase the gas can be transported through the soil or rock pores or open fissures and thus migrate great distances from the source of gas production.

2.2.1 Gaseous phase

The migration of methane gas through the ground in the gaseous phase is a combination of advection (pressure driven flow in accordance with Darcy's Law), and diffusion under a concentration gradient either by gas molecule to gas molecule (bulk diffusion) or gas molecule to soil molecule (Knudsen diffusion). A discussion of these migration processes is given by Hooker and Bannon (1993). The principles of advection and diffusion used to dilute and disperse gases in gas protection measures are discussed in Section 3.3.3. The migration of gas through soil is significantly influenced by the degree of saturation which in turn affects the permeability. In fully saturated soils where the pore space is full of water the flow of gas will be substantially reduced, i.e. the soil will have a low permeability to gas. High gas pressures or concentrations would have to be produced to cause gas migration through the pore space within the soil either by advection or diffusion. Unsaturated soils will be more permeable and, therefore, gas movement can potentially be much greater. Gas cavity expansion theory is a useful means of developing conceptual models of the permeability of soil to gas (Wheeler *et al.,* 1989).

In general, diffusion is the main process by which gas migrates from the ground to atmosphere (Baver *et al.,* 1972). Gas migration by diffusion from a source can occur in several ways. It may move through permeable strata or for considerable distances along faults, fissures or cavities in the strata. It can pass along man-made features such as mine shafts, roadways, sewers, or along the backfill around pipes or cableways. However, if gaseous exchange between the ground and the atmosphere is restricted by clay or other low-permeability medium, or a preferential path of relatively high permeability is formed, e.g. cracks or ground fissures or man-made openings (tunnels, shafts, etc.) then gas migration is likely to occur as a result of advection rather than of diffusion.

Rock fractures associated with mine working and ground subsidence have been reported as a pathway for methane migration to ground surface. Staff *et al.* (1991) discuss the migration of methane from longwall mineworkings and a number of incidents where mine gas has affected existing development. The potential for methane migration from longwall mine workings is shown in Figure 2. Abandoned underground mineworkings themselves can be extensive and offer an effective path for wide-scale gas migration affecting proposed and existing development in former mining areas.

A pressure gradient which will produce a mass movement of gas by advection may develop from the accumulation of gas in a confined space, e.g. after completion or capping of a landfill or from natural fluctuations in atmospheric pressure or in the elevation of the groundwater table in underground mine workings. Wind movement over the ground surface (*venturi* effect) and temperature gradient will also give rise to pressure differences (*stack* effect) and lead to gas migration.

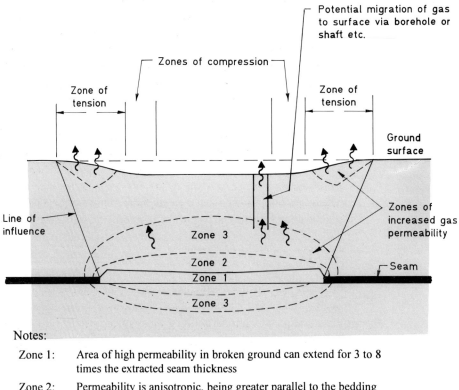

Notes:

Zone 1:   Area of high permeability in broken ground can extend for 3 to 8 times the extracted seam thickness

Zone 2:   Permeability is anisotropic, being greater parallel to the bedding plane than normal to it. Zone 2 can extend to approximately 100 m.

Zone 3:   Above and below Zone 2, there usually exists in coal measures relaxed strata known as Zone 3. The relaxation can be sufficient for the strata to become permeable, usually this is parallel to the bedding planes.

Figure 2   Potential for methane migration in longwall mining (after Staff et al., 1991)

It is known that changes in atmospheric pressure can cause a sucking or blowing of wells or shafts with the expulsion of mine gases as the underground pressure equilibrates with the new atmospheric pressure (Barry and Raybould, 1988). Water table fluctuations occur in response to barometric changes as well as rainfall and these may also affect the interchange of gas between the atmosphere and the ground. A contributory cause to the gas explosion at Loscoe, Derbyshire is believed to have been a very deep meteorological depression passing over the region. This is believed to have created a pressure gradient and the flow of gas from an adjacent landfill to the ground surface near houses. The increased gas emission rate into the void beneath the suspended ground floor of the property created an accumulation in methane concentration of explosive proportions (Williams and Aitkenhead, 1989).

Other influences on migration between the ground and the atmosphere include the degree of water saturation of the soil and ground freezing. Frozen ground or the downward permeation of rainwater may result in a significant reduction in porosity and permeability effectively sealing the ground surface (Barry, 1987). This may temporarily block existing migration pathways and allow new pathways to form, e.g. lateral rather than vertical pathways. Furthermore, gas may accumulate and only be released in large concentrations and volume as the temporary seal disintegrates. Gas migration by advection will tend to pose a greater risk to development because accumulation of gases and increases in pressure can occur in a short period of time not allowing adequate dilution and dispersion of gas.

Apart from the migration pathways associated with geological conditions there are many which are man-made and near the ground surface. Sewers, the backfill surrounding pipes or cableways, service ducts used for electricity, telephone, television cables, street light cables, water and gas pipes, drains and land drains may all provide pathways and/or voids (such as maintenance areas) along which gas may migrate and/or accumulate. The underground services which enter buildings provide pathways for gases into underfloor spaces and substructures where accumulation may occur giving rise to unsafe atmospheres (PSA, 1977 and Clow, 1991).

Made-up ground comprising relatively impermeable materials, e.g. concrete, clay or tarmacadam may also influence the migration route of an underlying methane source, by forcing the gas to travel laterally to another point or area of emergence. Under these circumstances high pressure gradients may build up creating an accumulation and sudden release of hazardous or explosive gas. These effects on the design of in-ground barriers to prevent gas migration are discussed in Section 5.

2.2.2   Gas in solution

Gases may not always exist in the ground in the gaseous form. They can be dissolved in the groundwater to an extent depending on the pressure, temperature and the concentration of other gases present and the dissolved mineral salt content in the water itself. Typical values of the solubility of methane and other gases in water are given in Table 4.

Table 4 Solubility of methane and associated gases in water

Gas	Solubility at temperature of 25°C and total pressure of 1 atm (mg/l)*
Methane	21.5
Carbon dioxide	1510
Carbon monoxide	0.275
Hydrogen sulphide	3850
Hydrogen	1.6

Note: * Total pressure is partial pressure of gas and water.

Dissolved gases may be advected by groundwater and only when the pressure is reduced and the solubility limit of the gas in water exceeded will they bubble out of solution and form a separate gaseous phase. Henry's Law describes the partition of a gas between the water phase and the gaseous phase as follows:

$$p_b = x_b . K_b$$

where
p_b = partial pressure of the gas (dimensions of pressure)

x_b = mole fraction of solute (dimensionless)

K_b = Henry's Law constant (dimensions of pressure)

From this equation it is relatively simple to calculate the amount of methane or other gases dissolved in water if the pressure and composition of the associated gas phase is known. Hooker and Bannon (1993) give further guidance on the solubility of methane and associated gases together with examples for calculating the concentration of methane in solution.

Henry's Law is valid for sparingly soluble gases. For carbon dioxide, however, Henry's Law holds at small pressures but significant deviations are found at high pressures. In general it is found that gas deviates from the law when:

- the concentration of the gas in solution is large owing to the solubility of the gas or the application of high pressures
- the nature of the gas molecule is altered in solution.

In the case of carbon dioxide, interaction with water leads to the formation of carbonic acid which in turn dissociates to a small extent into ions.

Table 5   Methane concentrations in some UK groundwaters (after Hooker and Bannon, 1993)

Groundwater	Methane concentration[*] (ml/l)	Partial pressure of methane (atm)	Temperature °C	Reference
In Chalk, London Basin, >70 m depth	$<1.7 \times 10^{-2}$	$<4.0 \times 10^{-4}$	10	Darling (1985)
Crystalline and metamorphic rocks, Scotland	$<1.3 \times 10^{-5}$	$<3.1 \times 10^{-7}$	10	Darling and Bath (1986)
Wessex Basin brines, 1700 m in Permo-Trias rocks	1.8	0.096	70	Darling (1981)
Carboniferous strata in Abbeystead tunnel	40	0.955	10	Bath et al.(1988)

Note: *   Methane concentration at a temperature of 0°C and total pressure (partial pressure of gas and water) of 1 atm.

Typical methane concentrations in some UK groundwaters are shown in Table 5. Methane can be dissolved to up to 3% by volume of water at 20°C and a pressure of 1 atm and this is equivalent to a concentration of approximately 22 mg/l. The migration of methane in groundwater over long distances followed by its release from solution to atmosphere can be a major problem. Buswell and Larson (1937) reported the occurrence of serious explosions in enclosed reservoirs and pumphouses as a result of pumping methane containing groundwater from wells.

At Abbeystead, Lancashire the explosion in the valve house with its attendant loss of life and injury is postulated to have been caused by groundwater containing methane. The groundwater, normally at a lithostatic/hydrostatic pressure equivalent to several hundred metres head of water, entered the tunnel which was at atmospheric pressure and resulted in methane bubbling out of solution (HSE, 1985 and Orr et al., 1991).

In normal shallow groundwater tables in the UK, such as those likely to be encountered during building development, the concentration of methane in solution is likely to be very low and is unlikely to influence design or construction.

However, many site investigation boreholes may reach depths of several tens of metres where, in certain environments in which there is an overpressured or confined aquifer containing gas, methane and associated gases could be released from solution. It is essential that such degassing is not allowed to occur in confined spaces such as beneath building development where a hazardous or explosive atmosphere could develop. Similar conditions may occur in deep basement construction where the design of the lowest slab requires control of underlying water pressures using permanent pumping. Drainage cavities are often constructed inside the perimeter retaining walls. These elements can trap gas released from solution into the drainage system.

2.3 ENTRY ROUTES INTO BUILDINGS AND SERVICES

As discussed in Section 2.2 there are many factors which can influence the natural migration of methane and associated gases from the ground to atmosphere. In certain situations therefore development can be seen as acting as a barrier to the natural migration of gas. In most cases the movement of gas is at very low concentrations and surface emission rates such that adequate natural dilution and dispersion into the atmosphere can take place at the ground surface. A barrier created by development will be insignificant in terms of the effect on changes in migration pathway, concentration and surface emission rate. However for development near or above gassing sources (e.g. landfill, mining areas, as outlined in Section 2.1) the concentration and surface emission rate may become relatively high such that natural dilution and dispersion becomes inadequate and gas accumulation occurs beneath the development. Furthermore gas may also be encouraged to migrate towards a building by advection because of a pressure gradient between the gassing source in the ground and the building interior. A slight negative pressure relative to atmospheric pressure can exist in a building as a result of the following two effects:

1. *Stack effect:* temperature differences causing difference between indoor and outdoor air densities (warm indoor air is less dense than cold outdoor air).

2. *Venturi effect:* wind moving across/around the external building fabric will draw inside air out through openings such as windows, doors, and building cracks.

Indoor air which is removed will be replaced by external air drawn in and this may include gas which may have accumulated beneath the building. Accumulation of gas and the increase in concentration will in turn increase the potential for gas to migrate through cracks and openings in the building by diffusion under a concentration gradient between the gas beneath the building and the internal air. Mechanical venting systems, e.g. fans, can also create a negative pressure with respect to atmosphere inside a building.

Thus a building or structure may tend to attract and collect gas as it naturally migrates from the ground. Figure 3 indicates the potential entry routes into a building.

Gas may enter a building/structure for the following reasons:
- gas-permeable materials
- design practices
- construction methods
- faulty workmanship.

Gas-permeable materials

The materials and products used in the construction of the building/structure fabric may themselves be permeable to gas, albeit to a greater or lesser extent. Methods for reducing the permeability of building materials are discussed in Section 4.1.

Key to ingress routes:

1. Through cracks and openings in solid concrete ground slabs due to shrinkage/curing cracks.
2. Through construction joints/openings at wall/foundation interface with ground slab.
3. Through cracks in walls below ground level possibly due to shrinkage/curing cracks or movement from soil pressures.
4. Through gaps and openings in suspended concrete or timber floors.
5. Through gaps around service pipes/duct.
6. Through cavity walls.

Locations for gas accumulations:

A.	Roof voids.	C.	within settlement voids.
B.	Beneath suspended floors.	D.	Drains and soakaways.

Figure 3 Gas entry routes into buildings

Design practices

Door and window frames which are apparently close-fitting may allow a substantial amount of air flow via gaps and cracks (Cherenko, 1974). These features may also allow the entry of gas into the building, particularly where the frame crosses the cavity between external and internal walls.

Another potential route of gas entry is via services and service ducts which enter the building and have, therefore, to pass through walls and/or the ground slab. All habitable building development will require ventilation with fresh air. This is absolutely necessary not only to provide a safe non-asphyxiant atmosphere but also to provide humidity and temperature control to prevent condensation and the growth of mould. For these reasons it is not possible to design a completely gas-tight building that will also be fit for habitation.

Construction methods

Construction of a building/structure necessitates fabrication of component parts and materials which by their very nature result in joints and openings, etc. Construction joints are also required to minimise ground and thermal movements. In addition, they are needed to control shrinkage/cracking during curing of cement and concrete construction. Failure to provide adequate joints can result in widespread random cracking difficult to identify and seal retrospectively. This can be a particular problem with large cast-in-place concrete ground slabs or rafts (see Section 4.1).

Standard of workmanship

Gas entry routes into buildings may frequently be because of defects due to the standard of workmanship in construction. This can also include installation of gas protection measures. Typical examples of defects are:

1. Inadequate construction joints in cast-in-place ground slabs/raft foundations together with inadequate steel reinforcement to control crack distribution (see Section 4.1).

2. The dpc and/or dpm as it crosses over a cavity wall is lapped but not taped, therefore allowing gas to migrate and accumulate in the cavity (see Section 8.2).

3. The use of low-permeability membranes at formation level laid on poorly compacted fill or highly compressible soils which subsequently settle and cause tears in the membrane allowing potential gas migration.

4. Service ducts inadequately sealed on the external cladding of a building.

5. Use of ground-bearing floor construction on poorly compacted fill leading to settlement, rotation and cracking of the slab.

6. Use of timber-framed housing construction where inadequate sealing of the timber frame to the concrete base/ground slab can result in gaps, which provide a potential entry route for gas from the cavity wall and beneath the internal wall. In addition, the method of fixing the timber frame to the concrete slab can result in micro-cracking of the slab allowing a potential migration path for gas entry.

2.4   BEHAVIOUR OF GAS IN BUILDINGS

Movement and mixing of gas with air within a building may take place under the actions of diffusion, turbulent jet mixing, buoyancy or turbulent interaction with ventilating air (Edwards, 1989). Of these processes, gas mixing by molecular diffusion is extremely slow. The effect of mixing is to dilute the gas progressively as the gas travels away from the point of ingress.

The factors which influence the movement and mixing of gas in a confined space are gas density, gas composition, rate of ventilation and location of the gas source. The density of the gas affects its buoyancy relative to that of air and this affects the tendency of the gas to form a layer either in the upper or lower part of the confined space.

The buoyancy of methane and carbon dioxide mixtures relative to air are shown in Figure 4. Guidance on the mixing of gases in buildings and their dilution and dispersion is given by Leach and Bloomfield (1974). Two conditions of gas mixing are recognised.

These are:

- instantaneous mixing
- gas layering.

In the majority of situations, gas mixing will occur in either of these two extreme conditions. It is possible, though, that a condition of gas mixing between these extremes could occur in some situations.

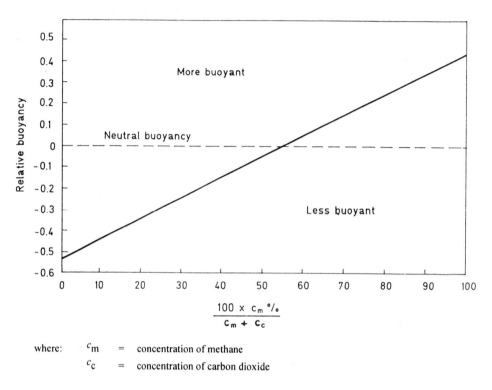

where: c_m = concentration of methane
        c_c = concentration of carbon dioxide

Figure 4 Buoyancy of methane/carbon dioxide mixtures relative to air

2.4.1   Instantaneous mixing

In practice gas entering a building will already be diluted with air. It will be further diluted by turbulent mixing with air within the building. For this reason the gas is likely to have neutral buoyancy within a short distance of the point of entry into the building. Under these circumstances the effect of buoyancy is negligible and instantaneous mixing of the gas will occur.

Experience has shown that where instantaneous mixing occurs the gas concentration stabilises at the ratio of the rate of gas entry to the rate of fresh air supply (NCB, 1979). Hence in the case of methane for example, to maintain the concentration below the lower explosive (LEL) (i.e. 5% by volume in air) would require a minimum volume flow rate of fresh air of 20 times the rate of methane entry. In habitable buildings instantaneous mixing is likely to predominate because of turbulence created by movement (e.g. opening of doors and windows) and natural ventilation. However, air movement within a building will depend on the use, size, layout and structural form and can be very difficult to quantify or model. For this reason the design of gas protection measures based on natural ventilation principles can be extremely difficult (see Sections 7.1.2. and 7.2.1).

2.4.2 Gas layering

In situations where there are significant differences between the density of ingressing gas and air, layering of gas will tend to occur. Layering can be difficult to remove if the rate of ventilation and air velocity are insufficient to disperse the gas.

In poorly ventilated buildings or confined spaces, tunnels, sewers, service ducts and chambers, gas layering may be a problem because of lack of ventilation inducing turbulence and mixing. In order to identify conditions in which gas layering may be a problem, a dimensionless quantity referred to as the Layering Number, L, can be applied.

$$L = \frac{U}{\sqrt[3]{g\left(\frac{\rho_g - \rho_a}{\rho_a}\right)\frac{q}{W}}}$$

where
U	=	ventilation velocity
g	=	acceleration due to gravity
ρ_a	=	relative density of ambient atmosphere
ρ_g	=	relative density of gas-forming layer
q	=	volume rate of ingress of layer forming gas
W	=	width of gas-forming layer

In horizontal tunnels layering of gas can be controlled if the air velocity is sufficient to maintain L at a value greater than 5 (Edwards, 1989). Hooker and Bannon (1993) give an example of the use of the Layering Number to calculate the velocity of air for ventilation and dispersion of a gas layer.

The position of gas ingress into a building or structure is also important. In substructure development, e.g. tunnels, sewers, service chambers or basements, gas ingress near invert level may establish a uniform concentration between the point of entry and the ceiling whereas a leak near the ceiling may result in a shallow ceiling layer of high concentration. The tendency for layering to form in a particular space depends on the direction of airflow or slope of structure gradient and the roughness and composition of the walls. Measures to prevent layering and gas accumulation in subsurface structures are discussed in Section 12.3.

2.5 HAZARDS AND DESIGN CRITERIA

Hooker and Bannon (1993) provide a detailed general review of the properties, hazards and effects of methane and associated gases. ICRCL Guidance Note 17/78 (1990) provides useful information on the properties and hazards of landfill gas. The hazards and effects of methane and associated gases are:

- flammability and explosivity
- physiological effects
- odour
- effects on vegetation.

All the gases are colourless and odourless in character except hydrogen sulphide and other minor or trace organic compounds (see Section 2.5.3). Table 6 summarises the hazardous concentrations of methane and associated gases with respect to toxicity and explosive limits, where applicable.

Table 6 Hazard concentrations of methane and associated gases (after BRE, 1977)

	Hazard concentrations	
	Toxicity of asphyxiation % by volume in air[1]	Explosive limits in air % by volume in air (LEL)[2] (UEL)[3]
Methane	30	5.0 – 15.0
Carbon dioxide	0.5	not applicable
Carbon monoxide	0.005	12.5 – 74.2
Hydrogen sulphide	0.0001	4.3 – 45.5
Hydrogen	30	4.0 – 74.0

[1] Eight-hour long-term exposure limit (HSE, 1991)
[2] Lower explosive limit
[3] Upper explosive limit

2.5.1 Flammability and explosivity

The greatest hazards posed by methane are those of fire and explosion. The limits of flammability of gas mixtures are affected by the composition of the mixture, strength of the ignition source, temperature, pressure and the nature of the surroundings.

The lower explosive limit (LEL) and upper explosive limit (UEL) of methane and associated gases are given in Table 6 It should be emphasised that concentrations above the UEL should not be taken to represent safety, because on dilution with air the composition might then fall within the flammable range. Where carbon dioxide is also present, the range of methane concentrations over which it is explosive is narrowed. When the proportion of carbon dioxide reaches 25% methane becomes non-flammable. If the ratio of carbon dioxide to methane is greater than 3.5, mixtures of these gases will not be flammable if mixed with air in any proportion. This ratio is known as the limiting safe mixture. However such mixtures may be seriously deficient in oxygen and may present an asphyxiation hazard (see Section 2.5.2). With regard to building development consideration should always be given to the potential variation in flammability and risk of explosion because of future changes in gassing regime. Further details and technical guidance on the limits of flammability of mixtures of gases are given by Hooker and Bannon (1993), ICRCL Guidance Note 17/78 (1990) and Edwards (1989).

A flammable gas or gas mixture is potentially hazardous when conditions exist which allow the gas to migrate from its source and accumulate in a confined space to a concentration between the LEL and UEL. A flammable mixture of methane and air will burn rapidly when ignited. If confined the deflagration generates high overpressures so that the effects are explosive. Beresford (1989) indicates three conditions which must be fulfilled for an explosion to take place:

1. There must be a source of flammable gas or vapour.

2. There must be an enclosed space in which the gas or vapour can accumulate with sufficient air to form a flammable mixture. Examples are building foundations and enclosed basements. Voids such as trenches, shafts or boreholes may also trap methane.

3. There must be a source of ignition. Examples are electric lighting, electric motors, sparks from metal contact, cutting and welding equipment, cigarette smoking, etc.

2.5.2 Physiological effects

The physiological effects of gases depend not only upon the toxicity but also upon degree, nature and length of exposure. The effects produced may appear in both the short and the long term. Local effects are produced at the point of contact with the body. Systemic or long-term effects are those produced by the gas or its metabolites on a whole range of bodily functions often far removed from the route of entry into the body. Effects may occur in the short term or may be delayed. The physiological effects of exposure to methane, carbon dioxide, carbon monoxide, hydrogen sulphide and hydrogen are described by Hooker and Bannon (1993) and Edwards (1989). Exposure to these gases by workers in confined spaces has been the cause of many injuries and fatalities. Occupational exposure limits to these gases is given by HSE (1992). Table 6 summarises the toxic or asphyxiant limits of methane and associated gases.

An important effect of accumulation of methane and/or associated gases in a confined space, e.g. tunnels, sewers or underground excavations, will be to displace air and thus reduce the total concentration of oxygen in the atmosphere. The normal concentration of oxygen in air is typically 19% to 21% by volume. Physiological effects of an oxygen-deficient atmosphere will vary with length of exposure and between individuals as summarised in Table 7.

Table 7 Effects of reduced oxygen concentration (after Edwards, 1989)

Oxygen % by volume in air	Physiological effect
19 – 21	Normal range of concentration in the atmospheric air.
17	Faster deeper breathing; slight impairment of judgement.
16 – 10	Initial signs of anoxia leading to emotional upsets, abnormal fatigue upon exertion.
10 – 6	Nausea, vomiting, unconsciousness; collapse may occur.
<6	Convulsions, gasping respiration, death.

If elevated carbon dioxide concentrations are accompanied by a reduction in oxygen concentration the effects can be more severe. Carbon dioxide affects the respiratory and central nervous system. At concentrations greater than 0.5% by volume in air it can cause unconsciousness leading to death at concentrations greater than 10% to 15% by volume in air. Its high solubility results in rapid diffusion and physiological effects are almost instantaneous.

2.5.3 Odour

While odour itself is not a hazard it can be an unacceptable long-term nuisance particularly if it is associated with gas ingress within a building. Methane and associated gases are themselves odourless with the exception of hydrogen sulphide (the smell of rotten eggs) and minor trace volatile organic hydrocarbons. Hydrogen sulphide is the most common reason for landfill gas odours, but this is not always the case. Trace organic hydrocarbons, e.g. mercaptans and alkyl benzenes, have been shown to be a major cause of odour (Young and Parker, 1984). Some of these trace hydrocarbons are also known to be toxic/carcinogenic, e.g. benzene, toluene and chlorinated hydrocarbons.

Odour thresholds are not only extremely difficult to estimate, but they depend on the individual, distance from source and on the presence of other organic compounds. Release of odorous gases may also be intermittent and dependent on weather conditions. Adequate dilution and dispersion is the most effective measure to render the gas odourless. Young and Parker (1984) suggest that, based on site measurements, a dilution factor of between 1000 and 10 000 can be required to render landfill gas odourless. For most landfill gas regimes encountered in-ground passive venting is sufficient to provide adequate dilution and dispersion (see Section 6.1). In circumstances where high concentrations and/or gas emission rates are encountered additional measures may be required. For in-ground gas protection measures these can include:

- passing the gas over activated carbon to absorb odours prior to release to the atmosphere, (Dorling, 1978): filters of this type can be fitted to vent stacks

- use of reodorants or deodorants

- active abstraction of gas and flaring to burn and destroy odours (see Section 6.2).

The removal of odorous gas emissions beneath buildings is more difficult. The use of membranes to prevent ingress of gas into buildings (see Section 8), in conjunction with in-ground venting to dilute and disperse gas, is possibly the most practical and effective solution.

2.5.4 Effects on vegetation

Strong correlations appear to exist between high concentrations of methane and/or carbon dioxide in soil and vegetation die-back especially in areas surrounding landfill sites (Barry, 1986). Current evidence indicates that carbon dioxide is toxic to vegetation in the root zone and that the principal effect of methane is to produce oxygen deficiency. The presence of both gases in the ground is therefore likely to be cumulative and especially serious at times of critical plant growth such as germination.

Most soils contain microbes which are capable of oxidising methane to produce carbon dioxide if air is present. Thus in soils in which methane oxidation is occurring, effects relevant to vegetation growth are the depletion of the oxygen content, the production of carbon dioxide and heating. Where the oxygen content is low the conversion of methane to carbon dioxide may be incomplete and intermediate products such as methanol, formaldehyde and formic acid may be produced. These can remain in the soil and exhibit phytotoxic effects to plants. Hydrogen sulphide, ammonia, benzene, ethylene, acetaldehyde and mercaptans which are often present in association with landfill gas are known to be highly toxic to plants (Kanol and Zether, 1990).

2.5.5 Design criteria

The degree of hazard from methane and associated gases and the consequent risk to development will depend on an assessment of the gas regime. This will involve knowledge of:

- the composition of the gas and individual concentrations of the component gases

- the rate of production of gas at source

- the gas emission rate at ground surface or exposed formation.

The assessment of risk will also require interpretation of ground conditions, hydrogeology and hydrology. In addition, an evaluation should be undertaken of the potential for future gas production and possible changes in the gas regime. This is because actual gas measurements recorded on a site may not necessarily be the appropriate criteria for assessing the need for protection and design of gas protection measures. For example, the effects of future development or changes on adjoining areas of land could affect ground and groundwater conditions such that the production, concentration and rate of emission of gas would also change.

Protection measures should be capable of maintaining air quality external to a building or structure below the hazard concentrations given in Table 6 at all times. In order to ensure this a margin of safety should be adopted when applying these hazard gas concentrations to the design of protection measures. This margin of safety should reflect:

- the inherent hazard posed by the gas

- the proposed end-use of the development and risk to occupants or users

- changes in gas regime over the life time of the development or the period over which the hazard remains present

- the uncertainty in gas measurements made, design principles and the fallibility of individual protection measures.

The reliability of measured gas concentrations and emission rates and the uncertainty of predicting future changes is probably the greatest influence on the design and application of gas protection measures. Without detailed knowledge of the gas regime and the long-term behaviour, gas protection measures cannot be fully designed or their performance guaranteed. This is one reason which has led to the adoption of high margins of safety on gas concentrations, the over-design of gas protection measures and the adoption of control systems based on a combination of individual measures (see Section 10).

Concentrations for methane and carbon dioxide which have been used as design criteria for gas protection measures are listed in Table 8. These gas concentrations are based on maintaining the general quality of air surrounding the building envelope to an acceptable level of risk. Reliance is made on natural dilution and dispersion of gas beyond the building envelope to further reduce gas concentrations to ambient levels in the atmosphere.

Table 8 Design criteria for methane gas protection measures

Gas	Design concentration % by volume in air	Reference
Methane	less than 0.25	BS 6164:1990 and Barry (1986)
Carbon dioxide	less than 0.25	Crowhurst (1987)

In other countries, North America and Scandinavia, design concentrations for methane and carbon dioxide are set at lower levels than those indicated in Table 8 to reflect ambient concentrations in atmospheric air (Fugler, 1992). The hazards and perceived risk to building development from gases such as carbon monoxide and hydrogen sulphide which are both highly toxic and explosive (see Table 6) demand their dilution and dispersion to concentrations reflecting standards for ambient atmospheric air. In the majority of situations where gas is released from the ground the concentrations of these gases are orders of magnitude less than methane and/or carbon dioxide. Gas protection measures designed to prevent methane and/or carbon dioxide accumulation should by implication normally be able to dilute and disperse the presence of these minor component gases.

3   Principles of protection

The hazards of methane and associated gases as described in Section 2.5 give rise to risks which should be taken into account in the design and construction of development. Several events in recent years have heightened public awareness of the dangers from methane and associated gases, e.g. the gas explosion at Loscoe, Derbyshire (Williams and Aitkenhead, 1989) and Abbeystead, Lancashire (HSE, 1985). Other occurrences and incidents involving gas explosions have been recorded by Baker (1987), Barry and Raybould (1988), Clow (1991) and Jaitly (1987). These events have raised the issue of protecting development with the aim of reducing risks to acceptably safe levels. However, in order to protect development all hazards should be adequately identified. This requires proper and comprehensive site investigation, including desk studies, exploratory fieldwork and gas monitoring to identify the nature of the gassing source, concentrations of individual component gases and rate of surface emission, including an assessment of the effects of temperature and pressure. Raybould et al (1995) address the issues of obtaining reliable and relevant information for the purposes of risk assessment. The higher the quality and extent of site investigation, including gas monitoring data, the greater the likelihood of selecting appropriate gas protection measures.

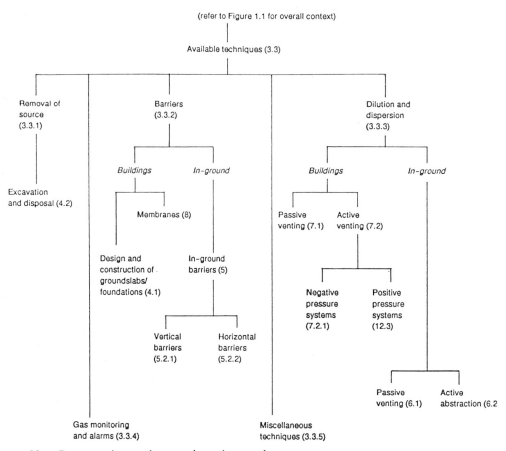

Note: Report section numbers are shown in parentheses.

Figure 5 Available gas protection techniques

The principles of protection to all forms of building development are similar, but the suitability and methods of application may often be different because of the constraints imposed by the nature of the particular development. This report recognises and discusses three main forms of development: new, existing and subsurface. Figure 1 indicates the broad layout of the report and how the principles of protection to these three types of development have been grouped. Figure 5 indicates the principal protection techniques referring to the relevant sections of the report.

It should be understood that, whatever protection techniques are used, absolute safety cannot be achieved, nor can a completely gas-tight building be constructed either in technical or economic terms. Such a structure would suffer from the effects of humidity and condensation because of the lack of adequate fresh air ventilation (see Section 2.3).

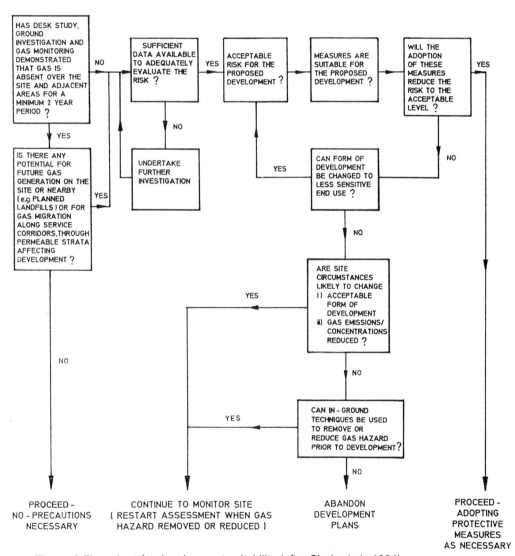

Figure 6 Flow chart for development suitability (after Clark *et al.*, 1991)

3.1   SUITABILITY OF DEVELOPMENT

Building design should aim to reduce the risks to development as far as possible to a safe acceptable level. Approved Document Part C2 of the Building Regulations (DoE, 1992) gives guidance for new development affected by methane or carbon dioxide and advice on construction techniques to minimise any risk. A problem arises in determining the degree of risk and what constitutes a safe acceptable level. Public opinion and attitudes change and although technical problems relating to gas protection can generally be overcome, other considerations such as legislation, economics, commercial marketability, maintenance of control measures and local authority requirements may preclude certain forms of development and/or gas protection measures.

The benefit and quality of living standards provided by the provision of services such as gas and electricity in the home gives rise to the public acceptance of their danger and risk. Incidents of gas explosions or fire in the home caused by faulty gas or electric equipment or connections have not deterred public opinion from accepting and using such equipment, e.g. gas or electric cooking stoves and fires. The assessment of risk from the hazards of methane and associated gases is the subject of a further report (O'Riordan and Milloy, 1995) in CIRIA's programme, *Methane and associated hazards to construction.*

In the case of new development a primary consideration is to judge whether the development proposed is suitable for its intended purpose based on a thorough knowledge and understanding of the ground conditions and the gas regime. In most situations, engineering solutions can be found to provide gas protection measures. However, certain types of measures may not be aesthetically acceptable or would be inappropriate to the nature of the development. For example, the use of in-ground active abstraction and the erection of vent or flare stacks within a residential development would jeopardise the commercial marketability of the properties, quite apart from difficulties in maintenance of the abstraction system. In these circumstances, better use of the land might be made by less sensitive end-use development in which the gas protection measures are acceptable to the general public, building occupants and owners. An example is using restored landfill for recreational purposes, parks, open spaces, etc., rather than building development. In these circumstances building development can be delayed until such time that the gas hazard is removed.

An alternative approach for new development is to remove/reduce the gassing regime prior to development using in-ground venting techniques to dilute and disperse gas (see Section 6). In this way the overall scope and level of gas protection measures required to buildings and structures can be reduced. For existing development the question of suitability and the option for changing the end-use does not arise. The approach adopted for existing development is discussed in Section 3.4.

A decision flow chart for evaluating development suitability and the appropriate form of gas protection measures is shown in Figure 6.

3.2   CONCEPTUAL DESIGN

In addition to development suitability an important issue to address is whether the conceptual design of the development or building is appropriate for the gas regime. In terms of the development layout the risks from methane and associated gasses in the ground may be reduced if buildings can be sited in areas which can be shown to have no or small gassing potential. Elsewhere areas of higher gas concentration and/or surface emission rate could be developed as open hardstanding or landscaped areas which can incorporate in-ground ventilation or barrier techniques without creating a hindrance or intrusion to the public and general environment.

Conceptual design of buildings/structures should address two important factors in relation to gas protection:

- the design and construction should itself provide a barrier to gas migration and ingress
- the design and construction should encourage dilution and dispersion of gas if, for whatever reason, it should accumulate beneath or within the building/structure.

In addition to the above factors, to ensure integrity and fitness for occupation, conventional building requirements and standards for protection against groundwater ingress, damp-proofing, thermal insulation, natural ventilation and fire precautions should also be met.

Some basic requirements for buildings which comply with the above factors are summarised in Table 9. Section 4.1 describes in more detail the basic requirements for gas protection. For certain types of development, particularly substructures such as basements, service chambers and ducts, etc., it may not be possible to provide and maintain a safe atmosphere because of the confined nature of the substructure and limited ventilation (see Section 12.3). In these circumstances the conceptual design of the substructure should incorporate a layout so that as far as possible routine access is not required to areas where hazardous gas is likely to be present or could accumulate.

In the specific case of methane, potential areas where a flammable atmosphere could exist should be separated from potential sources of ignition. In substructures in which there is any possibility of ignition of a flammable atmosphere, e.g. pump houses, service chambers, etc., they should be constructed to be blast resistant. Direct blast effects kill relatively few people in explosions. Flying debris and building collapse are a far more likely cause of death or injury (Thomson, 1987). Explosion pressures may be reduced by two orders of magnitude by providing sufficient openings, fixed louvres or blow-out panels. As an approximate guide a free area equal to one-eighth of the total surface area of a room/confined space is suitable (Beresford, 1989). Further guidance is given by NFPA (1988). The remainder of the building/structure fabric together with external and internal fittings can then be designed to resist the lower pressure.

Table 9 Basic considerations for gas protection of buildings

Barriers to gas migration and ingress	Dilution/dispersion of gas
• Use of low-permeability building materials and products, e.g. solid rather than cavity block works, mass concrete.	• Minimising downstanding beams, cross walls, etc., beneath ground slabs which provide confined spaces for gas accumulation.
• Use of low-permeability construction techniques, e.g. in situ mass concrete with steel reinforcement to reduce/limit shrinkage cracking.	• Considering provision of sloping underside of ground slab to encourage 'spillage' and dispersion to atmosphere of gas.
• Avoiding construction which provides joints/openings for gas entry, e.g. pot and beam ground slab construction.	• Maximising underslab ventilation by decreasing volume of undercroft and increasing spacing of vents.
• Use of precast suspended floor construction or raft construction to provide complete oversite barrier beneath structure.	• Detailing interior rooms for maximum ventilation and movement within acceptable limits.
• Limiting penetrations into the ground slab, particularly service entries.	

All electrical apparatus and circuits which cannot be located in safe, well-ventilated areas should be designed, installed and maintained for use in potential explosive atmospheres. BS 5345:1976 provides general information on the selection of appropriate electrical apparatus in potentially explosive atmospheres, while BS 5501:1977 provides recommendations for specific electrical apparatus. Further details regarding installation of electrical apparatus and the classification of potentially explosive atmospheres with regard to confined spaces in subsurface development are described in Section 12.3.

Box 2 Examples of conceptual design for new development

An example of conceptual design is the Stockley Park project in West London. At this former landfill site some $2.7 \times 10^6 \, m^3$ of gassing waste material was excavated and placed elsewhere on the site to form a recreational centre. The excavated material was replaced with some $1.15 \times 10^6 \, m^3$ of clean fill which was engineered and compacted to allow buildings to be constructed. The buildings have minimal gas protection which is provided by the installation of an in-ground barrier surrounding the gassing fill. The barrier comprises clay bunds and bentonite-cement cut-off walls. These techniques are described in Sections 5.4 and 5.6.

Other examples of the principle of conceptual design and construction are given by Fugler (1992). In Montreal, Canada, a 75-ha hi-tech industrial park has been constructed over gassing landfill. To minimise the potential migration of landfill gas into new industrial buildings, several units were constructed above ground on columns (incorporating piled foundations). A 'walk in' air space is provided between the original ground level and the floor of the building. To prevent migration of landfill gas into the building via sewers and drains, a pressurised plastic foul sewer system has been used with a passive venting concrete sewer system for storm water.

In the UK similar construction techniques have been used for office development with the air space beneath the ground slab designed as a car parking area. In this way the office accommodation can be isolated from any effect of gas by providing a passively vented underslab void (the car parking area) which provides ample dilution and dispersion of any gases emitted at surface.

In most types of new development it is possible to adopt a layout and conceptual design which reduces the risks from methane and associated gases to a minimum. Many protection principles are good engineering practice. Conceptual design and layout of residential developments are probably the most difficult to alter to minimise the risks from methane and associated gases. This is because from a marketing/commercial point of view a house or a flat should conform to certain traditional standards, fittings and layout which are acceptable to the public. To ignore these traditions would inevitably reduce the marketability of the property and its commercial value. Increased public awareness of the need for efficient use of energy resources in the design and management of buildings has led to greater insulation levels and reduced natural ventilation rates in new buildings. BS 8207:1985 provides guidance on the energy efficiency for buildings. This can result in recent buildings being less well ventilated to disperse/dilute gas if it should enter the building fabric. An example is the use of cavity wall insulation reducing natural air circulation in the void. A compromise may have to be achieved between low ventilation rates for energy efficiency and thermal insulation against adequate ventilation to ensure a safe atmosphere from the risks of methane and associated gases. In modern housing in the UK this may be difficult to achieve because of the high level of insulation and energy efficiency expected by the purchaser/ occupier.

In this connection the use of in-ground barriers (see Section 5) as a primary technique to prevent gas migration and surface emission occurring beneath buildings/structures will overcome the conflict between providing adequate gas protection measures to buildings and the need for energy efficiency. This conflict may also apply to existing development. Increasing the energy efficiency of an older building by the use of thermal insulation and sealants to reduce draughts, etc., may provide conditions for gas accumulation and increased risk to occupants (see Section 3.4).

3.3 AVAILABLE PROTECTION TECHNIQUES

The techniques of gas protection fall into two broad categories as follows:

- techniques for preventing or regulating gas emissions and migration from the gassing source, both from surface and subsurface boundaries
- techniques for preventing migration of gas into confined spaces within building structures and related infrastructure.

The techniques involved may range from rendering the site completely hazard free (by removing the gas) to providing barriers to prevent gas ingress. The degree of protection offered and the measures adopted will be site specific and will be influenced by many factors. It is important to realise that absolute safety cannot be achieved. As a general rule, therefore, gas-control systems should be designed as a combination of measures. Thus in the event of a malfunction or in-service failure there is at least one other measure to provide gas protection and minimise risk. The use of gas-control systems is discussed in Section 10.

In addition to the above there is a general requirement to ensure that any protection measures to development including infrastructure services can tolerate the effects of possible ground settlement. This is of particular concern particularly on landfill where future degradation of putrescible material can result in excessive differential settlement resulting in rupture of the installed gas protection measures. This may also be a problem on compressible soils (e.g. organic or peat deposits) and in land areas prone to mining subsidence. Allowance should also be made for the effects of future development on adjoining areas of land. Construction on adjacent gassing ground could well induce changes in the soil and groundwater regime which in turn might change the rate of emission and direction of gas migration possibly towards development elsewhere not protected from gas. A particular example is the installation of vertical in-ground barriers to control lateral migration of gas. The design of these barriers needs to take account of their influence on gas and groundwater flow in the surrounding ground and effect on adjacent land. The available techniques for gas protection are described below.

3.3.1 Removal of source

Generation and emission of gas may result from a variety of sources as discussed in Section 2. Removal of that source will render the site hazard free, assuming no residual gas remains in the ground and that all potential sources of gas have been identified and also removed.

The feasibility of such a method may prove acceptable for localised areas of gassing ground which can be readily identified. However, for widespread areas where multiple gassing sources exist the technique becomes impracticable, e.g. large landfill sites, abandoned mine workings and peat deposits. Section 4.2 discusses the various applications and suitability of this technique as a measure available for gas protection.

3.3.2   Barriers

If the gas source is outside the development/building area and the risk is because of gas migration it may be possible to isolate the development from the gassing source using a physical barrier placed in the ground or adjacent to the fabric of the building itself. No barrier is completely impermeable to the passage of gas or, indeed, fluids. In practice the design and installation of a barrier as a protection technique relies on its providing a greater resistance to gas migration that the surrounding ground so that gas is encouraged to migrate in another direction away from the development/building to be protected.

As discussed in Section 2.2, the main modes of transport for methane and associated gases in the gas phase are by advection and diffusion. The purpose of a barrier will be to prevent gas entry into the protected area. In practice this is achieved by designing the barrier to have a coefficient of mass permeability several orders of magnitude lower than the surrounding ground. Therefore any material or construction which has a mass permeability lower than the surrounding ground will act as a form of barrier by resisting gas flow. The lower its permeability the more effective it will be in preventing the passage of gas. Current UK practice is to design barriers, whether they be in-ground barriers or membrane applied to the building fabric, to have a resistance to the passage of gas equivalent to a material 1 m in thickness having a mass permeability of 1×10^{-9} m/s (HMIP, 1991 and NWWDO, 1988).

Table 10 Equivalent barrier thickness for given relative permeability

Material	Relative permeability of barrier[1]	Relative thickness of barrier[2]
Clay	1000	1
Polyethylene	280	0.28
LDPE	5	0.005
Modified bitumen and LDPE	1	0.001

Notes:

1. Information from Sheriff *et al.* (1991).

2. Thickness of barrier for equivalent permeability relative to clay.

This value for the required coefficient of permeability of 1×10^{-9} m/s is based on the permeant being water, and not to the transmission of gas. Work undertaken by Jefferis (1991) has shown that there is little correlation between gas and fluid permeabilities for any given material. This is particularly the case of in-ground barriers composed of clays and/or cements where changes in the pore size and pore distribution within the material can produce a gas permeability of the order of 10 to 100 times less than that for a fluid. The design of any barrier should take account of these effects and allow for potential changes in permeability either of the surrounding ground or the barrier itself. By altering the chosen permeability or thickness it is possible to produce a barrier from a wide range of materials with an equivalent resistance to the passage of gas as demonstrated in Table 10.

3.3.3   Dilution and dispersion

The purpose of dilute-and-disperse techniques is to reduce the accumulation of gas in the ground by allowing controlled release into the atmosphere. The release of gas is based on the principle that gas can migrate and disperse to the atmosphere from the ground by two processes. These processes are:

1. Molecular diffusion under a concentration gradient of the source gas in the ground, c, relative to the concentration of the gas in the atmosphere, c_a.

2. Advection or viscous flow under a pressure gradient, i, between the source gas in the ground and atmosphere. The pressure gradient can exist because of factors such as:

   - rate of generation of the gas at source
   - natural air movement creating areas of high and low pressure
   - barometric pressure change
   - air temperature change
   - groundwater level changes acting as a pump on gas within the ground.

Figure 7 indicates the principles of passive in-ground venting based on molecular diffusion and advection processes. Gas accumulation can result in an increase in concentration and pressure. This will lead to a greater potential for gas migration to take place across surface and subsurface boundaries (see Section 2.2). For this reason it is important that, when using barrier techniques to resist gas migration (see Sections 5 and 8), dilution and dispersion can also take place.

The technique of dilution and dispersion can be applied to gassing ground, e.g. by in-ground passive venting or active abstraction (see Sections 6.1 and 6.2). It is made to work by providing a zone or layer of high permeability material in the ground which has low resistance to the passage of gas. Thus gas is encouraged to migrate along this path rather than accumulate. Dispersion itself will not necessarily reduce gas concentrations since gas may still be present or continue to arrive from a gassing source. Indeed by providing an easier flow path the rate of gas entry may result in an increase in gas concentration if the rate of gas release to the atmosphere is low.

The technique can also be applied below buildings by incorporating passive or active venting measures (see Sections 7.1 and 7.2). The principle is to apply a pressure gradient between the underside of the ground slab and the ground from which the gas is being emitted to draw the gas out of the ground beneath the building. An additional advantage is that by maintaining a reduced pressure beneath the ground slab, air is encouraged to flow from the building through cracks and openings by the process of advection. In this way gas beneath the ground slab can be prevented from entering the building. The principles of design are described in Sections 7.1.1 and 7.2.1. Gas diffusion (although a continuous process) takes place relatively slowly and may not always be capable of diluting and dispersing gas sufficiently to reduce gas concentrations to safe acceptable levels for building development. For this reason the technique of dilution and dispersion is usually made to work primarily by the application of a pressure gradient. Gas diffusion is an additional secondary effect. In certain situations such as low gas regimes and/or in locations where accumulation of a gas can be tolerated, e.g. the accumulation of carbon dioxide beneath a gas-tight ground slab, dilution and dispersion by gas diffusion can be an acceptable principle for the design of gas protection measures (see Section 7.1). To discourage gas from passing through the ground slab a low-permeability gas membrane can be installed within the slab.

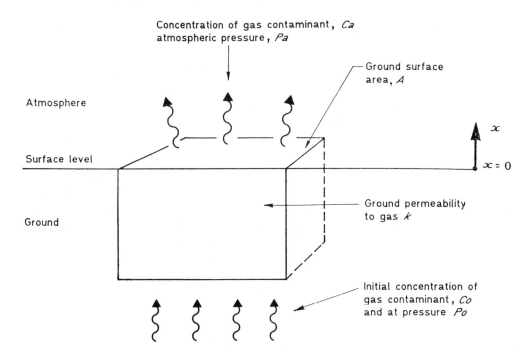

Concentration of gas contaminant, Ca
atmospheric pressure, Pa

Ground surface area, A

Atmosphere

Surface level

Ground

Ground permeability to gas k

x

$x = 0$

Initial concentration of gas contaminant, Co and at pressure Po

a) *Molecular diffusion of gas contaminant from ground source*
    The general equation related to diffusion is known as Fick's Second Law of Diffusion and is given by:

$$\frac{\delta c}{\delta t} = D^* \frac{\delta^2 c}{\delta x^2}$$

For one-dimensional diffusion from the ground surface of initial gas concentration c_o to atmosphere as a function of distance from the surface boundary at $x = 0$ and time t the general equation can be solved as $c(x, t) = c_o . erfc (x / [2 (D^*t)^{1/2}])$. D^* is the diffusion coefficient. The expression erfc (....) is the complementary error function which is obtainable from appropriate mathematical tables e.g. Freeze and Cherry (1979).

b) *Advection or viscous flow of gas contaminant from the ground source*
    One dimensional advection or viscous flow in a porous media can be determined using Darcy's Law which relates flow directly to pressure gradient and the permeability of the ground as:

$$Q = Aki$$

Q is the volumetric flow rate or flux rate of gas through a ground surface area A.
k is the effective coefficient of permeability of the ground to gas.
i is the rate of decrease of pressure with distance from the surface boundary in the direction of the gas flow where:

$$i = \frac{\delta P}{\delta x} = \frac{P_o - P_a}{x}$$

Figure 7 Principle of gas dispersion from the ground surface

In certain circumstances the application of a positive pressure can be used to dilute and disperse gas and offer protection to building development. Measures based on the principle of positive pressures are described in Sections 12.3. Such techniques are commonly used in tunnelling and coal mining (known as mine drainage) to dilute and disperse methane emission (Creedy, 1991). Positive pressure systems are used in North America and the Nordic countries as well as in the UK to exclude radon gas from building development.

For all these techniques the principle is to reduce gas concentrations and emission rates at the ground surface to a level below an acceptable design concentration for development/building design. Acceptable design concentrations and emission rates will differ depending on the nature of the gases present in the ground and their inherent hazards, the type of development and proposed end-use. Acceptable design concentrations for methane and associated gases are discussed in Section 2.5.5.

Dilution and dispersion techniques can be applied also to building interiors. In normal circumstances buildings will have been designed for adequate ventilation for habitation either by passive or mechanical ventilation. For this reason buildings will have a degree of in-built protection against gas ingress. However, a risk can develop where gas is allowed to accumulate in confined or poorly ventilated spaces or where there is a high rate of gas entry. The layout of new buildings should be designed with this in mind and suitable building details adopted to minimise confined spaces where gas may accumulate

3.3.4 Gas monitoring and alarms

Gas monitoring and alarms are an important aspect of gas protection. Technically they will not provide physical protection against the hazards of gas. However they are important in terms of risk management because they can:

- demonstrate effectiveness of protection measures installed, particularly if the gas monitoring information gathered at the investigation/design stage is sparse or of poor quality

- provide confidence to owners/occupiers that risk is under control

- identify malfunction in a gas-control system to enable remedial action to be taken

- keep owners/occupiers of a development involved in the overall long-term management of the gas protection measures

- identify reduction in gas levels and period of acceptable risk when system can be switched off, i.e. protection no longer required.

In many circumstances monitoring using portable meters/equipment will provide sufficient information. Alternatively, systems can be permanently installed to provide continuous monitoring with alarms if gas concentrations exceed safe acceptable levels. This may be justified in sensitive developments and where gas regimes are such that immediate attention would be needed (typical characteristic situations 4 to 6 of Table 28). It should be emphasised that the use of gas monitoring equipment and alarms should not be regarded as a replacement for permanent protection measures based on barriers or dilution/dispersion techniques. Applications of gas monitoring and alarm instrumentation to development are discussed in Section 9.

3.3.5 Miscellaneous techniques

Techniques for gas control have also been developed which rely on chemical or biochemical action. These techniques have been used with some success for inhibiting landfill gas generation from landfill sites, thereby reducing or preventing gas migration (Harries *et al.*, 1990). Inhibition of methane generation from landfill can be achieved by the use of chemicals including formaldehyde, methanol, ferric iron salts and nitrates. However, there are a number of difficulties in applying chemical inhibitors to landfill for the purpose of methane control. These include :

- difficulty of efficient dispersal of the chemical inhibitors throughout a large mass of landfill

- inhibition of many chemicals is often only partial

- chemicals themselves may be degraded by bacteria resistant to their effects

- costs of treatment can be high

- many chemical inhibitors are toxic themselves and their impact on the environment might be unacceptable

- a product of inhibition of methanogenesis can be increased leachate production from organic fatty acids produced in the waste degradation cycle.

Temporary inhibition of methanogensis in landfill might prove useful and practical, particularly as an emergency control, until more permanent gas protection measures can be installed.

3.4   DIFFERENCE OF APPROACH FOR NEW AND EXISTING DEVELOPMENT

In general terms the available techniques of gas protection described in Section 3.3 apply to both new and existing development. However, the suitability and methods of application are often different in view of the constraints imposed by existing development.

Table 11 highlights some of the more important aspects which lead to differences of approach between new and existing development. Usually gas protection measures for new development can be planned, costed and designed prior to development and occupancy of buildings. Because of this there is no immediate risk to the building development or future occupants, and gas protection measures can be made the subject of a thorough and well planned design review to obtain the optimum solution for the specific development and gas regime.

This review would include:

- technical design and efficiency

- practicality of installation and integration with the development/building

- conceptual design review of building/development to minimise the risks from gas (see Section 3.2)

- costs of installation and funding for long-term management.

In most situations relating to existing development there is unlikely to be scope to undertake a comprehensive review as there is an existing risk which requires immediate attention to safeguard occupants and possibly the general public. Decisions often have to be made on the basis of limited gas monitoring data. This can result in gas protection measures being installed which are conservative, because of the need to allow for unknown factors or scenarios which cannot be quantified at the design stage. This approach can lead to gas protection measures to existing development being conservative and possibly more costly. The use of gas monitoring and alarms in these circumstances can be beneficial (see Sections 9 and 11). A further problem related to existing development arises if there is a change of use of buildings with the result that modifications or alterations are undertaken which disrupt the operation of any installed gas protection measure. Difficulties of this nature are discussed in Section 11.3.

Table 11 Differences in approach between new and existing development

New	Existing
Identification of problem: Adequate site investigation and gas monitoring can be undertaken in advance of development to identify risks.	Risks from gassing ground not always identified until problem occurs.
	Gas protection measures may have to be chosen on the basis of limited data.
Ownership and land entry: Usually because developer owns land it is possible to undertake adequate site investigation, gas monitoring and installation of gas protection measures.	Can be difficult and time consuming to gain access to land or buildings in multi-ownership; this could have important bearing on selection of gas protection measures.
Landowner/developer will be committed to provide adequate gas protection measures to ensure development is safe and marketable.	Property owners may be reluctant to accept costs and need for gas protection, particularly individual private houseowners who fear blight to property.
Access/installation for in-ground protection measures: Little difficulty on undeveloped site to gain access for mechanical plant, etc., and install in-ground protection measures in desired locations.	Access for mechanical plant may be constrained by existing development/buildings and services.
Possible to install in-ground protection measures to disperse/dilute gas prior to development and thereby reduce overall level and need for gas protection.	May not always be possible to install in-ground protection measures in ideal locations and hence may not be fully effective.
Gas protection measures to buildings/ structures: Usually techniques can be incorporated in conjunction with routine building protection requirements for damp-proofing and ventilation; this results in cost-effective solutions as well as increased efficiency and reliability.	Cannot readily gain access to underside of building; thus choice of gas protection measures can be limited to sealing floors and walls to create barrier.
Gas protection measures can be designed and installed to suit development layout and usage.	Gas protection measures may not be ideal and therefore not fully effective; will usually require long-term gas monitoring to establish that the gas measures are effective.
Long-term management: Planning and long-term management of gas protection measures can be set up and funded with the aid of the developer and all interested parties, e.g. owners, occupiers, local authorities, utilities.	Difficult to obtain agreement to establish and fund long-term management of gas protection measures particularly land or property in multi-ownership.
	Local authority may be obliged to take up long-term management role on behalf of the community.

4 Basic requirements for gas protection

This section describes the basic requirements for gas protection which in theory can provide a hazard-free environment. There are two primary ways of protecting development. One is the design and construction of the ground slab or foundation to the structure to prevent gas penetration (Section 4.1). The other is the removal of the gassing ground (Section 4.2). Sections 5 to 8 describe more specific techniques which have been applied as gas protection measures. Reference should be made to Figure 5, which summarises these measures, and where they are described in the text.

In practice, the basic requirements for gas protection at best can only minimise the hazards of methane and associated gases to building development. This is because of the inevitable degree of uncertainty which is associated with engineering design and construction. Nevertheless, in the absence of other protection techniques the basic measures described in this section will have a significant influence in reducing the degree of risk.

4.1 DESIGN AND CONSTRUCTION OF GROUND SLABS

Properly constructed ground slabs can form a primary means of gas protection for many types of building. Mass concrete itself has a low permeability. Typically the permeability of mass concrete to water is of the order of 10^{-12} to 10^{-13} m/s. The permeability is influenced by the water/cement ratio and to a lesser extent by the aggregate/cement ratio. Permeability of concrete to gases is of primary interest in structures such as sewage tanks, gas purifiers and nuclear pressure vessels. The flow rate of air through concrete slabs (transmissibility) is of the order of 10^{-8} to 10^{-9} m³ per h/m² per N/m² pressure (based on a slab thickness of between 100 and 230 mm; Waters, 1960). Little information is available on permeability of concrete to various other gases, including methane. However, in general, the permeability of a concrete slab can be substantially reduced if the slab is reinforced. The use of steel reinforcement which conforms to the minimum percentages as given in BS 8110:Part 1:1985 can significantly improve the ability of concrete slabs to act as gas barriers by preventing thermal and shrinkage induced cracks.

Where timber floor construction is used it is normal practice that the underlying formation is blinded with mass concrete to prevent moisture/water vapour movement, etc., in accordance with the Building Regulations Approved Document, Part C, Section 4 (DoE, 1992) and Digest 364 prepared by BRE (1991a). The use of mass concrete as a blinding layer can also provide a barrier to gas.

Notwithstanding the low permeability of intact concrete, construction/movement joints and shrinkage cracks in concrete ground slabs will form the major pathways for gas migration, as discussed in Section 2.3. In view of the difficulty of preventing or sealing these features it is usual practice to use a synthetic membrane installed either within the slab or at formation level. The use of membranes is discussed in Section 8. In situations where the gas regime may be described as low (i.e. characteristic situations 1 and 2 as indicated in Table 28) a cast in-place ground bearing or suspended floor concrete slab is likely to provide sufficient gas protection. Ground-bearing slab construction should only be used where ground settlement is unlikely. Construction joints between wall and floor slab may act as pathways for gas entry, particularly if these joints 'open' with future ground movement and settlement of the floor. This can lead to rupture of the membrane and gas ingress. For high gas regimes, it is more usual to combine the ground slab with underslab passive or active venting to prevent continued accumulation of gas and increase in concentration (see Sections 7.1 and 7.2). In these circumstances suspended ground-slab construction with an open or filled void arrangement will be required.

Typical details of suspended ground-slab construction are shown in Figures 31 and 33. Where underfloor insulation is required it should also be detailed so as not to interfere with free movement of gas. Ideally, a crack-free suspended floor should be provided by a ground slab cast in place under strict control to minimise shrinkage and curing cracks. This can be achieved using protection layers and steel reinforcement. For small buildings, such as housing, the ground slab should be designed to span one way between cross-walls, with a flat smooth soffit free of downstanding beams which might impede dilution of gas and dispersion. Dore (1983) provides useful guidance on the design and construction of concrete ground slabs for small buildings.

Cast-in-place concrete slabs with a void beneath can be difficult and costly to construct because of the need to use permanent formwork. For this reason a common method of forming suspended floor slabs is the use of beam and block construction. Such construction, however, can provide multiple pathways for gas migration around and through the blocks. This type of construction should be avoided on gassing sites unless combined with the use of underslab passive or active venting to prevent accumulation and a membrane across the slab to prevent migration of gas into the building.

In certain ground conditions the use of rafts to form the ground slab/foundation can be adopted. This will minimise the number of construction joints and thus limit the frequency of cracks and openings as potential migration pathways to gas. A typical detail of raft construction is shown in Figure 8.

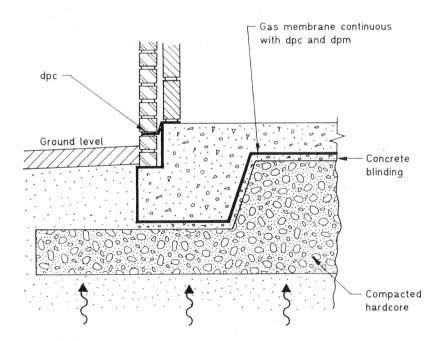

Figure 8 Typical raft construction

A problem of this type of construction is that gas can accumulate beneath the soffit of the raft slab and be trapped by the edge beam unless some form of venting arrangement is incorporated. Depending on the nature of the gas this may be an acceptable risk. However, in most situations it is best avoided and this can be achieved by incorporation of vents to allow any gas to disperse by passive venting as described in Box 3. Alternatively a gas membrane can be laid at formation level beneath the raft. Another means of preventing gas accumulation is to design the raft with sloping soffits to encourage movement and dispersion of gas, towards the external edge as shown in Figure 9. This type of construction is difficult and rafts will usually require edge thickening to distribute wall loads and provide rigidity, a requirement which can conflict with the principle of a sloping soffit.

Box 3 Example of raft construction on gassing ground

For a terrace housing development in the Midlands raft construction was proposed. The ground conditions comprised deep structural fill (foundry sand) overlying coal measures strata. Gas was detected in the fill at concentrations up to 1% and 5% methane and carbon dioxide by volume in air respectively. A cross-section of the raft is shown below.

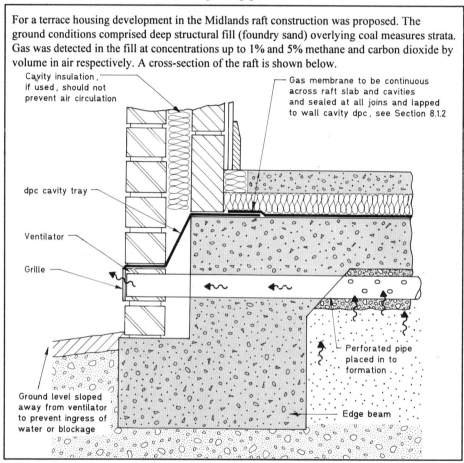

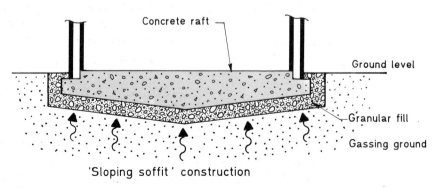

'Sloping soffit' construction

Figure 9   Principle of modified concrete raft used for gas protection

On larger buildings with wide floor spans design and construction of a gas-proof cast-in-place suspended ground slab is more difficult. This is because of the need to provide:

- possibly deep downstanding beams to provide slab rigidity
- movement joints in the slab to allow controlled expansion/contraction.

Deep downstanding beams can allow gas to accumulate beneath the slab soffit. For this reason beams should be perforated at frequent intervals typically by 100-mm diameter holes across the neutral axis at slab soffit level to permit unhindered movement of gas. Movement joints formed in the ground slab can be sealed with a gas-resistant mastic sealant. Guidance on the detailing of joints and steel reinforcement to limit curing and shrinkage cracking is given by Deacon (1987). In addition, formwork used to cast the slab soffit cannot always be recovered from the restricted underslab void and can interfere with the venting measures. An example of the use of shuttering for the construction of a wide span cast-in-place suspended slab is given in Section 8.2. Prestressed slabs have been used to provide a gas-tight floor for large buildings (Rys and Johns, 1985).

4.2   EXCAVATION AND DISPOSAL

In the UK, excavation and disposal is commonly used in the redevelopment of contaminated sites, including those containing gassing wastes. The method involves excavation of the gassing material and its replacement with clean, inert fill. By its very nature, removal of the gassing material provides a permanent solution for those sites by eliminating the gas source and the potential for long-term or continuing gas migration affecting the development. Nevertheless, gas protection measures, e.g. passive in-ground venting, may be required while residual gas levels remain in the ground (see Section 6.1). The advantages of removal have to be balanced against its higher initial capital cost compared with other protection options described below. However, an exception to this is the excavation and disposal of coal which can be linked to opencast coal mining or reworking of former colliery/mine spoil tips. In these circumstances revenue gained from coal working can be used to pay for excavation and disposal costs to remove the gassing ground source. An example of this is given in Box 23.

Generally, excavated material is removed off site and transported to a suitable disposal site licensed to accept non-inert waste. This is a feasible and cost-effective option where the gassing material is present in discrete, easily identifiable places and of relatively small volume, and where the disposal site is reasonably close. After excavation, the replacement fill should be clean, inert material, i.e. free of major constituents which might themselves be a potential source of gas. Peat or organic soils, landfill, inert fill containing timber, coal or minestone can be sources of methane. Calcareous fill materials such as chalk or limestone, in an acidic soil or groundwater environment, may result in the production of carbon dioxide. The use of these materials as infill should be assessed lest the need for gas protection from their use would negate any benefit gained by removal of the primary gassing source.

Usually it will be necessary to compact the infill in order to prevent excessive self-weight settlement. Areas of deep infill or where structures are to be founded will require careful placement and compaction to prevent unacceptable settlement. Ground improvement including special foundation techniques may also be required to ensure settlements are within acceptable tolerances for building development. CIRIA Special Publication 78 (Leach and Goodger, 1991) gives useful guidance on the engineering problems and remedial treatment of filled sites.

Where the quantities of gassing materials are large or there is no local disposal tip, excavation and reburial of the gassing waste on site can be a feasible alternative. Reburied material should be far enough away from the development in an area where any gas migration can be prevented. This is often best achieved under areas of landscaping isolated from structures. Current government legislation may require both planning permission and issue of a waste-disposal licence from the appropriate waste regulation authority to rebury any contaminated or gassing waste. The site licence will require the buried gassing waste to be placed in an engineered containment cell designed and constructed to prevent any migration of leachate or gas. In-ground barrier techniques to form containment cells are discussed in Section 5.

An important aspect is that exposure of the gassing source upon excavation can give rise to health and safety risks not only to construction workers but also to the general public. The risks are particularly great where large excavation and disposal operations are involved on land which has been contaminated by industrial processes and is also generating gas. These risks include combustion/explosion/physiological and odour effects and dust (see Section 2.5). For these reasons, excavation operations need careful control. Useful guidance on safe working practices on contaminated sites is given by the HSE (1991) and Barry *et al.* (in preparation).

Box 4 On-site excavation and reburial for development

An example of on-site excavation and reburial is given by Gordon *et al.* (1987). They describe the development of a 140-ha commercial and leisure development on a former rubbish tip which involved the excavation and reburial on site of an estimated $2.7 \times 10^6 \cdot m^3$ of gassing landfill. The reburied landfill has been contained by the use of engineered clay bunds, and bentonite/cement slurry trench cut-off walls (see Section 5.5) with passive venting trenches (see Section 6.1.2). Its completed design provides a championship golf course and amenity area.

Removal of contaminated material can pollute surface and groundwaters, particularly if excavation is below the water table, with possible serious detrimental effects on the quality of potable water sources. Under current UK legislation (Control of Pollution Act, 1974; Environmental Protection Act, 1990; Water Resources Act, 1991), the polluter of a surface or groundwater source can be prosecuted and made to undertake remedial measures to clean up the pollution. In areas of high water table operations associated with excavation, reburial of gassing material and infilling with clean inert fill can change the hydrogeological regime, both beneath the site and within the surrounding area. To maintain the hydrogeological regime, drainage measures and associated recharge systems may have to be constructed.

5 In-ground barriers

5.1 DEFINITION AND APPLICATION

In-ground barriers are widely used in the UK to control gas migration. The barrier is constructed of a material of a very low permeability, relative to the surrounding ground, to resist gas passing through. It is installed in such a way as to isolate the development from gas migrating through the ground. In-ground barriers have been used to prevent migration of gas affecting both new and existing development (see also Section 11.1). In most applications some form of in-ground venting arrangement on the 'gas' side of the barrier will also be incorporated to prevent accumulation of gas and build-up of pressure. Gas is encouraged to migrate towards the venting system and disperse to atmosphere. Passive or active in-ground venting techniques which are used in conjunction with in-ground barriers are discussed in Sections 6.1 and 6.2.

A wide range of methods and materials has been used to provide in-ground barriers. Most of these methods developed from waste management practice for the control of landfill gas and leachate migration from operational or closed landfill sites. DoE (1986), NWWDO (1988) and Fung (1980) provide guidance on both natural and synthetic barriers, installation techniques and their likely behaviour in a landfill environment. Table 12 gives a summary of the types and materials used to form in-ground barriers which are discussed in this section.

Table 12 Various methods and materials used to form in-ground barriers for gas protection

Type	Position	Natural clay	Synthetic liner	Admixed materials	Mass/ reinforced concrete	Steel piles
Horizontal	At surface	Prepared formation place and compact (5.4)	Prepared formation place and roll (5.5)	Not appropriate	Prepared formation (5.2)	Not appropriate
	Underseal at depth	Not appropriate	Not appropriate	Grouting techniques (5.7)	Not appropriate	Not appropriate
Vertical	Depth up to say 8 m	Backfilled trench or open excavation (5.4)	Backfilled trench or open excavation (5.5)	Backfilled trench or open excavation (5.6)	Backfilled trench, secant piles (5.8)	Driven sheet piles (5.8)
	Depth greater than 8 m	Not appropriate	Slurry trench cut-off (5.6)	Slurry trench cut-off (5.6), grouting (5.7)	Diaphragm wall, secant piles (5.6)	Not appropriate

Note: Report section numbers are shown in parentheses.

A recent development in barrier technology is the use of vertical glass walls (Holzman, 1991). An in-ground barrier is formed by glass panels joined by high density polyethylene (HDPE) sliding locks. The panels are inserted in a bentonite or bentonite/cement slurry trench and can be arranged to form a single or double row interlocking vertical barrier. A permeability to liquids and gases of the order of 10^{-13} m/s is reported. The glass wall is highly resistant to chemical attack and is therefore suitable for aggressive ground conditions such as landfill or contaminated land sites. However, the use of this type of barrier could be limited to situations where long-term ground strains are likely to be small.

5.2 PRINCIPAL TYPES OF BARRIERS

In principle, two types of in-ground barrier can be considered to control gas migration affecting development. These are:

- vertical barriers to form a cut-off against lateral gas migration towards a development

- horizontal barriers to prevent gas migration directly beneath the development.

Both types of in-ground barrier are shown in Figure 10. Factors which will influence the type of in-ground barrier selected are:

- ground and groundwater conditions

- nature and extent of the gas and source material itself

- whether the protection to be afforded is temporary or permanent.

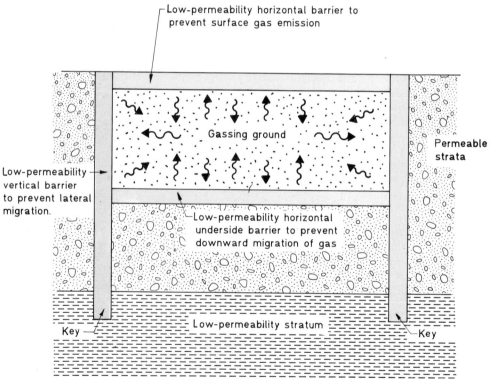

Figure 10 Principal types of in-ground barrier

Vertical barriers

Where there is a suitable natural layer of low-permeability material at depth beneath the gassing source, a vertical barrier 'keyed' into the low-permeability layer can be used to prevent lateral gas migration towards development. In certain situations the groundwater table can be considered as an effective impermeable horizon to prevent methane gas migration. However, to be successful it should be clearly demonstrated that methane cannot be dissolved into the groundwater and be transported beneath the barrier, and that the groundwater table will not be lowered below the base of the barrier. A vertical barrier can be installed to surround the gassing source and isolate the proposed development from the risks of gas migration. Alternatively, where the gassing source is remote from the development the barrier can be constructed to intercept and thus direct gas migration away from the site. The principal uses of vertical barriers are shown in Figure 11.

The design of a vertical barrier should consider also the effects on surrounding land and existing development. Construction could induce changes in the groundwater regime resulting in groundwater level rise upstream of the barrier because of any impounding effect. Changes in groundwater level can change the rate of gas emission and direction of gas migration. This aspect should be allowed for in the design and installation. An example of this is given in Box 24.

Horizontal barriers

The main purpose of a horizontal gas barrier is to prevent gas emission at the ground surface, usually over a large area of the development. The barrier comprises a low-permeability layer carefully placed and sealed around services, foundations and substructures. A wide range of materials can be used including remoulded clay, mass concrete or synthetic liners. Descriptions of suitable materials, the methods of their installation, and their application are discussed in Section 5.4 and 5.5 (Section 8 discusses the specific use of synthetic liners as gas barriers within the building fabric of a development). Usually, the horizontal barrier will be underlain by a venting blanket or gas drainage layer. Further details of venting blankets or gas drainage layers are given in Section 6.1.2.

Techniques based on injection of grout or jet grouting can also provide horizontal barriers to prevent gas migration through a high permeability stratum at depth beneath a site. This is also known as bottom sealing or undersealing. Such techniques have been used successfully beneath new and existing development to seal mine shafts and fissured ground associated with coal mining from the effects of methane gas (Raybould and Anderson, 1987). Chipp (1990) described the use of inclined interpenetrating walls formed by a cement:soil mix-in-place process to form a seal at depth beneath a landfill site to control gas and leachate migration. Childs (1985) describes various methods based on grouting techniques of forming in-ground horizontal underseal barriers to contain contaminants or pollutants. The techniques of installing horizontal underseal barriers are still in the development stage. They are likely to remain of limited value for the purposes of gas-control in that it will be difficult to ensure complete integrity.

5.3   REQUIREMENTS AND MATERIAL SELECTION

Materials used to form an in-ground barrier have very different characteristics and are suited to different applications. The barrier requirements which will influence material selection are:

- permeability
- stress/strain characteristics
- resistance to chemical or biological attack
- durability.

These requirements are discussed below.

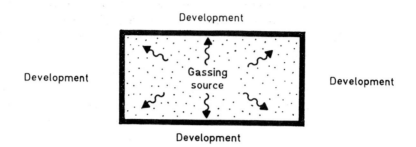

(a) Vertical barrier surrounding gassing source

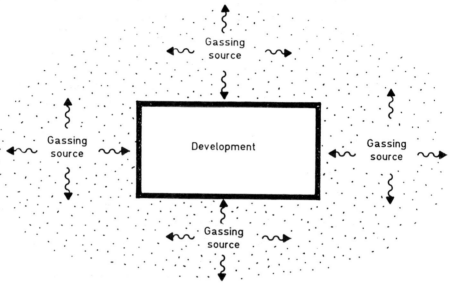

(b) Vertical barrier surrounding development

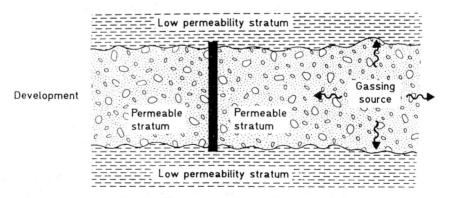

(c) Single vertical barrier to prevent gas migration through permeable stratum

Figure 11 Principal uses of vertical barriers

Permeability

An extremely low permeability is the single most important requirement of any in-ground gas barrier. Current waste management practice is to specify a permeability equivalent to a coefficient of permeability of less than 1×10^{-9} m/s for landfill liners to control gas and leachate migration (DoE, 1991 and NWWDO, 1988). Current UK practice is to adopt this same value of permeability for the design of in-ground barriers against gas migration even though there is no useful correlation between the gas and water permeabilities for any given material (Jefferis, 1991). Limitations on the relevance of defining a permeability for in-ground gas barriers are discussed in Section 3.3.2.

The permeability to gas of in-ground barriers formed of clay, soil/bentonite mixtures or bentonite/cement hardened slurry or mass concrete varies with their composition and water content. If these types of materials are fully saturated then there can be no gas migration other than by diffusion through, or advection with, water (see Section 2.2.2). However, if the material dries out it may shrink and crack, and become locally very permeable. In the partially saturated state the menisci in the pore water of the barrier effectively block migration unless the pressure of gas is sufficient to force the water from the pore space and establish a flow path. The pressure necessary to do this is likely to be high and thus the partially saturated material may still be an effective barrier, particularly where gas pressures can be prevented from increasing by the use of in-ground venting techniques. However, for barriers formed of bentonite slurry admixtures a small loss of water may open up flow paths of quite significant proportion increasing the permeability of the barrier to gas by several orders of magnitude (see Section 5.6.2).

Stress/strain characteristics

A barrier material should have good resistance to physical damage, particularly to puncturing, and to processes that may lead to rupture such as elongation (in the case of barriers formed of synthetic liners) or erosion (in the case of natural clay barriers). For natural materials this characteristic depends to a large extent on the method of placement and compaction. However, one of the advantages of using materials incorporating bentonite is its self-sealing property (see Section 5.4). Synthetic liners may also be damaged in transport by careless handling and during installation, and liner properties should be chosen to take account of these possibilities.

Resistance to chemical and/or biological attack

It is essential that the material is resistant to the known or anticipated components of the gas and the ground and to any aggressive constituent of the source material itself, including soil microbial activity.

Durability

An in-ground barrier has to remain intact for a long time while the possibility of gas migration remains. This could be for at least the lifetime of the development. For commercial or retail development this might be as short as 10 to 15 years, but for private residential housing it might be for 50 to 100 years or longer.

There is very little field information on the long-term resistance and durability in aggressive ground conditions (e.g. contaminated land and landfills) for most of the in-ground barriers discussed in this report. A consequence of a breakdown in the integrity of the barrier could be a large increase in gas permeability and the potential for migration. An important factor which can influence the durability of an in-ground barrier is its tolerance to surrounding ground movement. Where ground movement could be large, e.g. landfilled ground or areas subject to potential mining subsidence or collapse, the durability and integrity of a barrier is likely to be limited. However, it is often the case that future ground movement is unknown or cannot be predicted with any certainty at the time of design of the gas protection measure.

For this reason an in-ground barrier can seldom be relied upon as the sole protection measure to development. Other measures, particularly in-ground venting, should always be incorporated into the overall gas-control system (see Section 10).

5.4 NATURAL SOIL BARRIERS

The most common natural materials used in the UK to form in-ground barriers are remoulded clay and soil/bentonite mixtures. Both horizontal and vertical barriers can be formed using these materials.

5.4.1 Clay

The requirements for remoulded natural clay to form a satisfactory low-permeability in-ground barrier have been reviewed by Oweis and Khera (1990). Factors such as particle size, moisture content, method of compaction and placement are all important if a natural clay barrier is to perform satisfactorily. Table 13 summarises the advantages and limitations of clay in-ground barriers.

The use of clay in-ground barriers specifically for gas-control is a very recent development in the UK. From the information gathered as part of this report most of the barriers have been constructed within approximately the last five years and then mostly in connection with new landfill development.

Gas monitoring data to measure performance and effectiveness are sparse. At best, gas monitoring for a short period after construction will have been carried out but is likely to have ceased after the stipulated construction maintenance period.

In-ground barriers have been used longer in the USA and Canada and some European countries for the control of leachate and gas from landfills and much published information is available from these sources, e.g. Oweis and Khera (1990); Goldman et al. (1986); Childs (1985) and Fung (1980). In summary, the findings from these sources indicate that:

- some clays may not be resistant to specific caustic and organic substances; this is particularly important in contaminated ground or landfill environments
- clay may not be acceptable where absolute containment to leachate is required as well as to gas; it will shrink and crack if allowed to dry out.

Such potential effects could allow gas migration through the barrier in the long term.

As discussed in Section 3.3.2, it is not always relevant to specify a permeability value for compacted clays. Mitchell (1976) demonstrated that the permeability of a clay compacted wet of its optimum moisture content may be more than three orders of magnitude lower than that compacted dry of optimum. Clay for use as an in-ground barrier should be tested to ascertain its compaction and permeability characteristics prior to use. These tests will determine the optimum range in moisture content to place and compact the clay to achieve minimum permeability both in terms of gas and water.

A typical relationship between the compaction of clay and permeability is shown in Figure 12.

Box 5 Use of vertical in-ground clay barrier

An example of the use of a clay bund is at Stockley Park, in the London Borough of Hillingdon, where a clay perimeter bund of 2 m thickness was constructed around the entire building development area to eliminate the possible entry of methane and/or leachate (DoE, 1989b). A section through the bund is shown in the figure below. The bund comprised recompacted London Clay won from the base of the excavation after removal of the landfill from the building areas (see also Box 4).

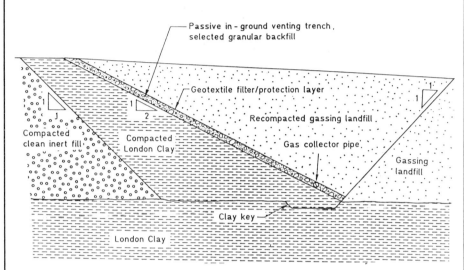

In order to ensure low permeability, the compaction specification required that the re-compacted clay should have:

- a dry density of not less than 90% of the maximum dry density determined using British Standard BS 1377:1975, Test 12

- a moisture content in the range of -1% to +4% of the optimum moisture content

- not more than 5% air voids.

The bund was 'keyed' into the underlying *in situ* London Clay to form a fully contained in-ground barrier against the migration of methane and leachate. A 600 mm wide granular blanket was placed between the clay bund and the landfill to allow gas to vent passively to atmosphere. (The application of venting trenches is discussed more fully in Section 6.1.2.)

Box 6 Use of horizontal in-ground clay barrier

Crowcroft *et al.* (1991) describe the construction of a new motorway service area near Thurrock, Essex. A compacted clay horizontal in-ground barrier which also incorporates a polyethylene membrane has been placed over the site beneath the development which comprises amenity building, motel, refuelling area and parking facilities. The barrier was laid across some 40 acres of an infilled quarry, some 20-m deep and actively producing landfill gas. The horizontal barrier prevents landfill gas emission at ground surface affecting the development. The landfill gas is vented from beneath the horizontal barrier using active in-ground abstraction techniques, (see Section 6.2). Details of the long-term management procedures at this site are presented in Box 32.

Table 13 Advantages and disadvantages of clay in-ground barriers

Advantages	Disadvantages
• Suitable clay may be readily available on site.	• Clay requires very close control of moisture content to achieve the chosen degree of compaction and low permeability.
• The plasticity can be changed to lessen the risk of cracking and rupture from adjacent soil movements.	• Difficult to compact adequately in a trench excavation to form a vertical in-ground barrier, best placed as earthworks fill.
• Techniques for handling and placement are routine in civil engineering.	
• Unlike synthetic liners, clay does not need special jointing.	
• Clay may be cheaper than alternatives, depending on local availability, required volume and access, etc.	

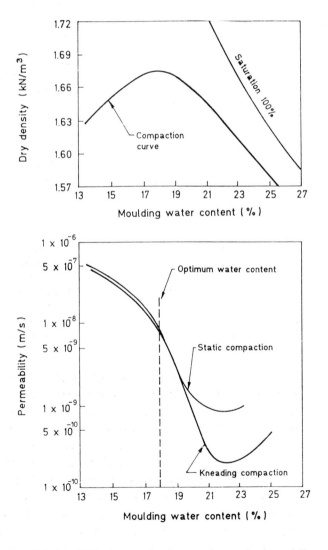

Figure 12   Relationship between clay compaction and permeability
(after Mitchell, 1976)

5.4.2   Soil/bentonite mixtures

High-swelling clay minerals have been widely used to control excessive seepage in natural soils by filling the void space between particles and thus decreasing their permeability. Bentonite is one of the most widely used clays for this purpose. Bentonite is also used as an admixture with cementitious materials to form low permeability in-ground barriers. These types of barriers are discussed in Section 5.6.

Bentonite is the commercial name given, originally, to a natural sodium clay of volcanic origin mined in Wyoming, USA. The chief constituent of bentonite is the clay mineral montmorillonite. The sodium form of bentonite has the characteristic of swelling to 10 to 15 times its dry bulk volume when placed in water. It is this swollen mass that fills the voids in soils that reduces their permeability. This property is used in soil/bentonite mixes to form a material with a low coefficient of permeability to form an in-ground barrier.

Table 14 Advantages and disadvantages of soil/bentonite for in-ground barriers

Advantages	Disadvantages
• The addition of bentonite to a wide range of soils can provide a material of lower permeability.	• Soil/bentonite is not suitable to form a low-permeability barrier if the soil is a coarse material such as gravel.
• The material requires no special jointing.	• Placement is generally restricted to flat surfaces or gentle gradients where sufficient compaction can be achieved with mechanical plant. It cannot be adequately compacted in a narrow trench to form a vertical barrier.
• The swelling properties of soil/bentonite overcome susceptibility to puncturing and a degree of self-healing.	• It is vulnerable to shrinkage and cracking if allowed to dry. Also, it may be vulnerable to attack in aggressive groundwaters including salt water and certain industrial wastes which can impair the swelling properties of bentonite; the use of specially formulated bentonite (saline seal) can be used which after hydration and swelling will not deteriorate as rapidly when exposed to high levels of ionic contaminants (Fung, 1980).

Natural sodium bentonites have very high swelling properties and are used extensively in the USA to form soil/bentonite low-permeability liners for landfill containment. These are principally horizontal in-ground barriers with soil/bentonite bunds forming the sides of the landfill. Some 3% to 6% by dry weight of bentonite is added to the chosen soil; often a sand with a clay and silt content of up to 20% or 30% is used (Oweis and Khera, 1990). The actual design mix is determined from laboratory and site trials to produce a material with the desired degree of permeability. In the UK, naturally occurring bentonites are generally of the calcium form and do not exhibit high swelling characteristics. Calcium bentonite can be converted, however, to the sodium form by the addition of up to 4% of sodium carbonate by weight of bentonite. The converted bentonite does not fully develop the properties of natural sodium bentonite however, and usually has to be in greater proportions in soil/bentonite mixes.

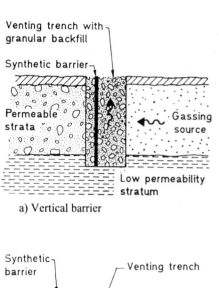

a) Vertical barrier

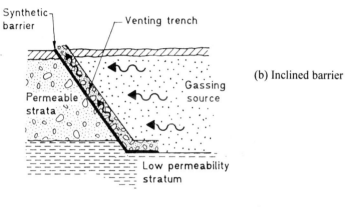

(b) Inclined barrier

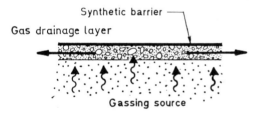

(c) Horizontal barrier

Figure 13 Use of synthetic barriers

The soil/bentonite mixture is prepared on site in a central mixing plant and placed using similar earthwork procedures and compaction criteria to those for a natural clay liner (Section 5.4.1). Useful information on the methods and specification for the installation of soil/bentonite liners are given by NWWDO (1988) and Fung (1980). Table 14 summarises the advantages and limitations of soil/bentonite in-ground barriers. High-swelling clay minerals have been widely used to control excessive seepage in natural soils filling void space between particles and thus decreasing their permeability. Bentonite is one of the most widely used clays for this purpose. Bentonite is also used as an admixture with cementitious materials to form low-permeability in-ground barriers. These types of barriers are discussed in Section 5.6.

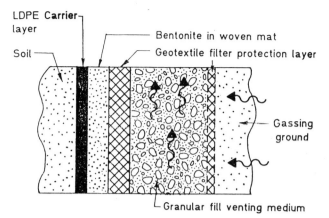

(a) composite synthetic barrier with bentonite

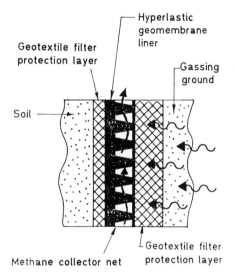

(b) composite synthetic barrier with synthetic venting blanket

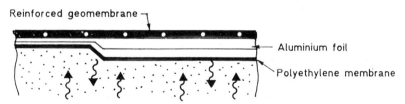

(c) composite synthetic barrier with aluminium foil

Figure 14 Typical details of some composite synthetic barriers

5.5 SYNTHETIC BARRIERS

Synthetic barriers, also known as flexible membrane liners (FML) or synthetic liners, are used predominantly for the containment of landfill sites to control both leachate and landfill gas migration. In the USA the use of synthetic barriers is mandatory for containment of hazardous waste landfills. In the UK the National Rivers Authority policy on groundwater quality protection (NRA, 1991) is likely to make the use of synthetic barriers a requirement for new landfill sites and also as part of the remediation measures for clean-up of contaminated land. Figure 13 illustrates the typical applications of synthetic barriers.

5.5.1   Material properties

The most common synthetic barriers are thermo-plastics formed from polyethylene, polypropylene, and polyvinyl chloride (PVC) either used individually or combined as copolymers. General descriptions of some synthetic liners are summarised on Table 15. Further guidance is given by DoE (1986), NWWDO (1988) and Oweis and Khera (1990). Additives may be incorporated in the material to improve its properties. Within the last five years or so there appears also to be a trend to combine the synthetic liner with other materials to form a composite liner. This has been used particularly where a low-permeability in-ground barrier to gas as well as pollution migration is required, i.e. in a landfill environment. Figure 14 gives typical examples of some of the more widely used composite liners for gas-control. Composite synthetic barriers for prevention of gas migration include low density polyethylene (LDPE), or high density polyethylene (HDPE), laminated with aluminium foil. The foil has an extremely low permeability to gas. The polyethylene acts as a carrier sheet and protects the aluminium from damage by careless handling and placement. Other composite synthetic barriers include a thin mat enclosing a layer of bentonite powder which is bonded to a carrier sheet of LDPE. In the ground the bentonite when hydrated and swollen is reported to have a coefficient of permeability to water in the order of 10^{-10} m/s.

Table 15 Materials used for synthetic in-ground barriers

Liner	Description
Polyvinyl chloride (PVC)	Widely used for lining waste treatment lagoons in the USA, has not been used in the UK. It is available in unsupported sheeting up to 0.75 mm thick having good tensile strength properties and resistance to mechanical damage. It is also resistant to many inorganic chemicals, but is weakened by hydrocarbons, solvents and oils. Its useful life is limited to about 20 years since the plasticiser that forms up to 40% of its composition is slowly leached out or volatised. Loss of plasticiser causes the liner to become brittle and therefore susceptible to stress cracking.
Neoprene	Is similar to a natural rubber in flexibility and strength, but has improved resistance to weathering and mechanical damage. Neoprene is resistant to dilute solutions of hydrocarbons and oils. Its main disadvantage is its high cost and the need to use adhesives for seaming.
LDPE	LDPE is available in thin sheets up to 1 mm in thickness. It is highly flexible and inert to most halogenated and organic based solvents. However, it offers poor puncture resistance and will suffer mechanical damage if badly handled on site; difficult to join in the field. Installation costs are low. Should be formulated with carbon black or other ultra violet light absorbers to improve weatherability.
HDPE	HDPE is available in thicknesses up to 3.5 mm. The greater thickness than LDPE and its formulation offers increased strength and resistance to puncture and abrasion. However it has limited flexibility. Liable to creep when subject to stress. Has good resistance to wide range of chemicals and solvents. Widely used in the UK for landfill lining, ponds, etc..

Polyethylene has been used in the UK for the last decade or more, and is the most favoured material for synthetic barriers (NWWDO, 1988). It is manufactured in sheets of various sizes and thicknesses and is usually coloured black (by the addition of carbon black up to 2% by weight) to resist the effects of ultra-violet light, which can cause embrittlement.

Proprietary brands of polyethylene liner are usually either high density (HDPE) or low density (LDPE). High density indicates a high percentage of crystallinity (i.e. less void space) and vice versa and because of this HDPE has a lower permeability to gas. HDPE is usually available in thicknesses of 1 to 3.5 mm. Low density polyethylene is thinner, at 0.5 to 1 mm, but the sheets are normally reinforced with a polyester ribbing (scrim). The suitability of HDPE and LDPE is summarised in Table 16.

Table 16 Suitability of high and low density polyethylene in-ground barriers

Material	Advantages	Disadvantages
HDPE	Transmissibility of intact material to gas is extremely low and virtually impermeable; values are of the order of 5×10^{-10} m³/m²/s and 20×10^{-10} m³/m²/s for methane and carbon-dioxide respectively at a pressure of 1 atm (Haxo, 1975). Relatively easy to lay depending on sheet size. High resistance to puncture. Thick enough for joint faces to be cleaned by grinding to remove any contamination prior to welding; less likely to burn through during welding. High elongation at break, e.g. it can accommodate substantial deformation if there is settlement or movement without rupturing (but note that some commercially available makes of HDPE have greater elongation in one direction than another).	Large sheet can be difficult to handle. Thicker sheets typically greater than 1.5 mm are less flexible, especially in cold weather, and expansion in hot weather may cause rippling.
LDPE	Transmissibility of intact material to gas is low (but not as low as HDPE) of the order of 25×10^{-10} m³/m²/s for methane at a pressure of 1 atm. The light weight of the material means that very large sheets can be laid quickly and with less jointing. High elongation at break, typically greater than 800%. Flexibility allows undulations of the formation to be followed closely.	Lower puncture resistance than HDPE, although extent of ruptures is likely to be limited because of the reinforcing scrim. Weld temperature needs very careful control to avoid burning through the sheet. Low elongation at break when reinforced.

In general, synthetic barriers can offer advantages over natural materials in terms of their availability and ease of placement and installation. However, it is generally agreed that all such synthetic barriers will leak to some degree.

This leakage is not through the synthetic material itself, which is essentially impermeable, but through holes or other defects produced during manufacture, handling or installation. Depending on the type of synthetic material and quality control procedures, it has been estimated that there could be some two to 50 holes per hectare of placed liner (Giroud and Bonaparte, 1990) of which two thirds are associated with seam welds (Pegg, 1989). Typical causes of leaks are:

- improper sealing of joints and welds
- carelessness in installation resulting in puncture holes
- physical damage caused by backfill material
- effects of ground movement causing elongation and cracking
- chemical or biological attack
- a particular problem of horizontal barriers is inadequate venting causing uplift by build-up of gas beneath barrier, resulting in rupture.

5.5.2 Methods of installation

Synthetic barriers can be installed in:

- open excavation
- trench excavation
- slurry trench cut-offs.

Figure 15 In-ground synthetic barrier placed in open trench

Trench excavation

In the majority of situations there is limited land available to create an open excavation either because of existing development or other physical site constraints. In these circumstances the synthetic liner is installed within a trench excavation. For depths to 5 m or so, a trench can be excavated using conventional plant and proprietary trench support systems. The liner is placed in the trench as a continuous roll and the trench backfilled. It is advantageous if the depth of the trench is less than the width of the roll. In these circumstances the liner can be placed as a continuous roll into the trench as excavation proceeds, as shown in Figure 16. Welding of joints is only required between rolls of synthetic liner and is thus kept to a minimum. By reducing the frequency of welds the integrity of the liner is greatly increased.

Box 7   Installation of synthetic barrier in a bentonite/cement slurry trench cut-off

Ingle and Kavanagh (1991) describe a case where low-permeability gas barriers were installed in a 470-m long slurry trench cut-off at Queslett landfill site, Birmingham. A 2-mm thick HDPE liner was delivered to site pre-cut to the required depth and in widths of 5.1m. To install the liner, a purpose-built steel frame was manufactured. The liner was offered up to the steel frame and tensioned into position. The liner and frame were then lifted by service crane and placed centrally in the slurry trench. A second lifting frame and liner was lined up to the interlock of the first frame and the second liner homed into the trench. The first liner was then detensioned from the frame which was then extracted from the trench. The sequence of excavation and installation was repeated to form the completed wall. The completed wall is shown below.

Installed barrier

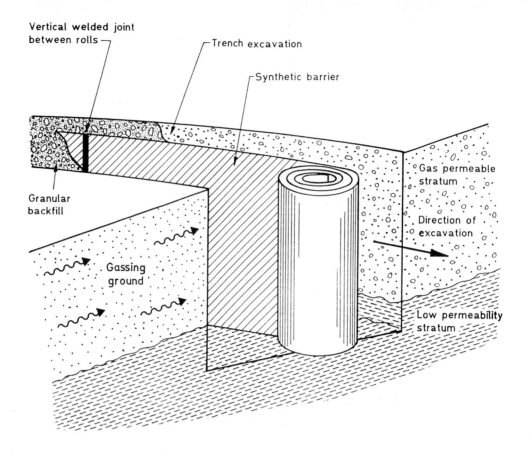

Figure 16 Installation of synthetic barrier in trench excavation

Box 8 Testing of a synthetic barrier in a slurry trench

At Poole, Somerset, a test cell was constructed as shown below to demonstrate the integrity of the synthetic barrier and its joints. The void formed between the two synthetic barriers was regularly monitored for the presence of methane which might have migrated into the void from the surrounding ground. If gas was detected it would demonstrate failure of the synthetic barrier or the interlock joints or both. The results of an on-going monitoring exercise have detected no methane in the test panel although methane concentrations in the surrounding ground have been recorded as up to 15% by volume in air.

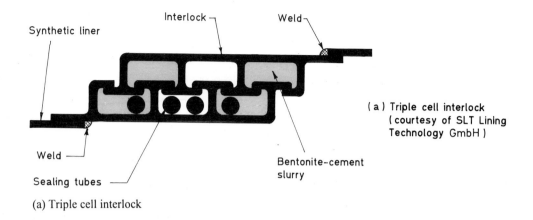

(a) Triple cell interlock

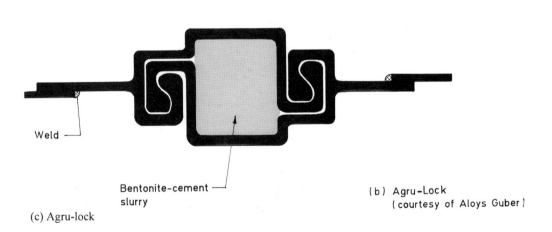

(b) Geolock system

(c) Agru-lock

Figure 17 Types of interlock system used for synthetic barriers

An example of this type of installation is given in Box 25 which describes a case to protect existing development from landfill gas migration. The backfilled excavation also acts as a passive venting trench to prevent accumulation of gas in the ground (see also Section 6.1.2). Figure 22 and Box 25 show typical construction details of synthetic barriers in closed and open venting trenches.

Slurry trench cut-offs

Where the required depth of in-ground barrier is greater than the excavating depth of conventional plant, the synthetic liner can be installed in a bentonite/cement slurry trench cut-off (see Section 5.6). In this situation special techniques are required to place the liner into the cut-off trench in such a way to ensure complete integrity. An example of this type of installation is given in Box 7.

A critical factor in the success of this type of in-ground barrier is the interlocking of each panel liner to form a gas-tight seal. Several different joint systems are available, but all require considerable care in use. Typically a membrane panel may be over 10 m high by 5 m wide and mounted on a heavy metal frame. The panel joints therefore must be robust and simple to use. Three proprietary types of membrane incorporating interlock systems are shown in Figure 17.

Problems of synthetic barriers installed in this way include:

- poor manufacture of interlocking joint welded to liner, resulting in tears on site during handling and placement
- problems of sealing interlock with sufficient penetration of slurry (see Section 5.6)
- stress fracturing of interlock due to high localised pressure around joint during installation and mating of barrier panels
- installed liners bending or buckling in the trench, causing rupture at joints and not forming an adequate seal at base of excavation
- difficulty of sealing services which cannot be re-routed and pass through the in-ground barrier (see Section 12.1).

For the above reasons, it is important that the installed synthetic barrier is tested in situ in order to demonstrate its integrity and ability to prevent gas migration. This can be achieved by the construction and testing of a test cell. An example of the use of a test cell is given in Box 8.

5.6 BENTONITE SLURRY ADMIXTURES

Barriers constructed from a bentonite slurry with the addition of an admixture such as natural soil or a cementitious material are more commonly called slurry trench cut-off barriers or hydraulic cut-off walls. They have been widely used in the USA and Europe since the mid-1940s to form deep in-ground barriers to groundwater movement. In the past five years or so they have been used in the UK to protect existing and new developments from gas migration as well as containment of leachate at landfill and contaminated sites. The main advantage of these types of barriers is that they can be constructed to depths significantly deeper than those using conventional excavating plant working in an open unsupported trench. Barriers as deep as 120 m have been constructed using bentonite/cement slurries as both the trench support fluid and the long-term hardened barrier. Construction to these great depths can be achieved by use of a clam shell crane-mounted rig.

5.6.1 Principles of design

Bentonite slurries have been used as stabilising fluids in deep excavations since the late 1930s. A trench filled with fluid can be kept open and excavated to almost any depth without the risk of collapse (Jefferis, 1972). For this purpose the fluid should exert sufficient hydrostatic pressure to maintain trench stability and it should not drain away into the ground to an unacceptable extent. These requirements are typically met with a bentonite slurry or a bentonite/cement slurry because of their density and their ability to seal the pore spaces of the sides of the trench.

Once a trench has been formed, the component that will be the in-ground barrier can be installed. This may be concrete (though the costs tend to limit the use of concrete to structural piles or diaphragm walls, see Section 5.8), a clay/cement or clay/cement/ aggregrate plastic concrete, a soil/bentonite mix or a synthetic liner. A further adaptation is to excavate the trench under a bentonite/cement slurry which is designed to remain fluid during the excavation phase but which will set and harden when left in the trench to form a material with permeability and strength properties similar to those of a stiff clay (Card, 1981). These slurries are known as self-hardening slurries and are the most widely used form of cut-off in the UK. In the USA, soil/bentonite cut-offs are often used for groundwater control, but it appears that synthetic liners are preferred for pollution and gas-control. In Germany, a chemically modified high-density soil system has been developed and appears to offer superior performance in terms of impermeability though at a substantial cost.

Jefferis (1990) has reviewed the permeability of slurry trench cut-off barriers to leachate and gas in relation to their mix design and requirements for long-term strength and durability. The normal criteria for such walls are:

- a minimum strain of 5% without failure by cracking, to provide sufficient flexibility to ensure the integrity of the wall under compressive, tensile and shear forces
- a maximum strength and minimum permeability to provide a degree of durability
- suitable rheological properties to provide pumpability and to ensure trench stability both by the action of hydrostatic pressure and 'filter cake' formation.

For strain at failure to be greater than 5% will require the barrier to be formed of a low strength material. However, a low permeability requires a high clay and cement content. The clay content is in turn limited by the desired rheology of the slurry. High clay contents will lead to an unmanageably thick slurry (in contrast cement content has a rather more limited effect on the rheology unless very high concentrations are used). Durability also requires a high solids content and particularly a high clay content. Thus the design constraints are:

- low clay content to give a fluid slurry
- low cement content for high strain at failure
- high clay and cement contents for low permeability
- high clay (and cement) content for durability.

The design of bentonite/cement slurry materials requires achieving a compromise. Traditionally, for groundwater control a permeability of only 10^{-8} m/s was normally specified, which was relatively easy to achieve for a mix with a strain to failure of 5% at low confining stresses. However, the requirement for a permeability of 10^{-9} m/s makes this much more difficult (unless an age at test of the order of one year rather than the usual 28 days is specified). The permeability requirements for in-ground barriers are discussed in Section 3.3.2. If both the early permeability and strain to failure are the determinants then a synthetic liner will be needed. While this may be appropriate it should be noted that there are many existing walls designed to 10^{-8} m/s which are behaving satisfactorily as in-ground barriers for gas-control (Jefferis, 1990).

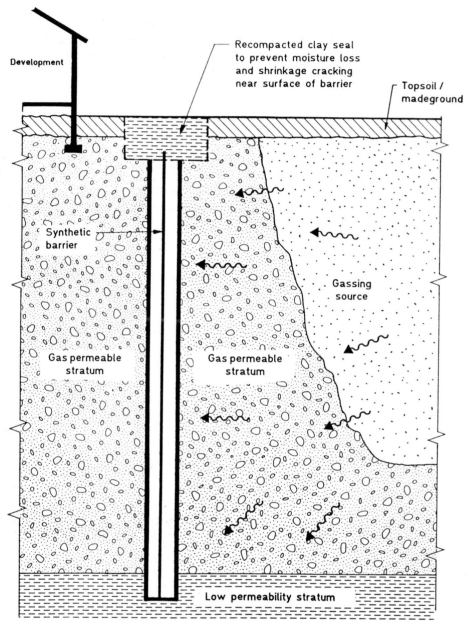

Figure 18 Typical installation for bentonite: cement in-ground barrier incorporating a synthetic liner

5.6.2   Types of slurry trench cut-off barriers

There are now a significant number of different types of slurry trench cut-off barriers which have been used for pollution control including gas. Childs (1985) and Jefferis (1990) describe some of the most widely used materials together with details of their mix composition and properties. Most slurry based cut-off materials have relatively high water content. If this water is lost they may shrink and crack and become gas permeable. Reported main causes for water loss and cracking of slurry trench cut off walls are:

- evaporation at or near the surface of the wall resulting in significant shrinkage cracks within the top 1 or 2 m

- in-ground heating of the wall from the heat generated within gassing ground, e.g. landfill

Labels in figure:
- Development
- Recompacted clay seal to prevent moisture loss and shrinkage cracking near surface of barrier
- Topsoil / madeground
- Synthetic barrier
- Gassing source
- Gas permeable stratum
- Gas permeable stratum
- Low permeability stratum

- segregation of materials and bleeding of water in the slurry leaving channels (syneresis) and permanent cracks in the hardened wall.

Other causes of cracking in slurry walls have been attributed to the formation of bubbles or pockets of gas due to migration from the surrounding ground. These factors need to be considered in the design and installation of these walls. Types of slurry trench cut-off barriers are described below.

Soil/bentonite cut-off

This is formed by excavation under a bentonite slurry and backfilling the trench with a blended soil/bentonite mix which forms the low-permeability element. General design procedures for soil/bentonite backfills to slurry trench cut-off barriers are given in D'Appolonia (1980). The backfill in a soil/bentonite cut-off has to have a high water content so that it will self-compact when placed in the trench. Unfortunately high water content clay systems will always be vulnerable to loss in moisture as discussed above. This may cause significant shrinkage and loss of integrity of the barrier.

Bentonite/cement cut-offs

These are now regularly employed in the UK for groundwater and pollution control including that for methane and associated gases. Clay/cement slurries are usually self-hardening slurries simply left in the trench to set at the end of excavation. Examples of this type of installation are given in Boxes 7 and 24.

Bentonite/cement/aggregate cut-offs

The addition of aggregate reduces the quantities of bentonite and cement required to form a wall. The addition of aggregates, however, can be more than just a filler as the mixes tend to be stronger and stiffer than bentonite-cement systems but also less plastic. The strain to failure may be low, especially if the aggregate particles are in grain-to-grain contact. This may be difficult to avoid unless the slurry is specially thickened so that the aggregate particles can be held in suspension prior to set. The reduced contents of clay and cement and the potential for cracking at slurry-aggregate interfaces make these types of barrier less durable in pollution control systems, other than with specially designed aggregate gradings.

Cut-offs with synthetic liners

The inclusion of synthetic liners is appropriate where there are high levels of pollution or very aggressive chemicals within the environment. A synthetic liner can be obtained to resist a wide spectrum of chemicals. Given the general uncertainty of the permeability of a bentonite/cement wall to gas (see Section 5.3) and the potential for cracking, the addition of a synthetic liner should be considered essential where long-term integrity and gas containment are required.

The major problems with the installation of synthetic liners relate to the sealing of the membrane to the base of the excavation and the joint between liner panels. The base seal is achieved by mounting the membrane on a frame and driving the whole assembly a pre-determined distance into the base of the trench. This operation has to be undertaken with some care to avoid damaging the membrane and the inter-panel joints (see Section 5.5.2). Details of jointing systems are given by Krause (1989). Figure 17 illustrates three types of jointing systems.

Typically a bentonite/cement trench is of the order of 600 mm wide. The insertion of a membrane will substantially disturb the behaviour of the slurry in the trench and the membrane can act as a plane of discontinuity and encourage cracking at the interface. Therefore if a membrane is used it should be treated as the sole impermeable element and the bentonite/cement solely regarded as providing support and mechanical protection. Typical configuration for this type of in-ground barrier is shown in Figure 18.

High density walls

These are relatively new cut-off materials developed specifically for polluted ground. The slurry comprises sodium silicate, pulverised fuel ash and/or sand together with a chemical additive to cause setting and hardening. The hardened material is hydrophobic and its water permeability can be very substantially lower than that of conventional soil/bentonite or bentonite/cement. Indeed, the permeability may be so low that diffusion becomes the most important transport process. Chemical resistance to aqueous pollutants is better than for conventional slurry walls. However, material costs are higher and special excavation plant may be necessary because of the high density of the slurry which follows from the high solids content. Details of the system are given by Hasse and Hitze (1986).

5.7 BARRIERS FORMED BY GROUTING TECHNIQUES

Three main techniques have been used to form in-ground barriers. These are:

- grout injection
- jet grouting
- vibrated beam grout injection.

These techniques are described below.

Grout injection

This may be defined as the injection of appropriate fluids under pressure into the ground through specially constructed holes in order to fill and seal pore spaces, voids, cracks, seams or fissures or other cavities in soils and rock strata. The result or objective is to establish a soil or rock mass with very low-permeability characteristics. In general a coefficient of permeability of the order of 10^{-7} m/s is regarded as reasonable for grouting operations used in groundwater control, but the actual value will depend on ground type. Bell (1981) discusses the general types and methods of grouting for general ground improvement. Leach and Goodger (1991) discuss the application of grouting techniques to the *in situ* treatment of contaminated land.

Cement-based grouts have been used to form in-ground barriers to methane migration. In suitable soils and rocks grouting can be carried out at any depth and hence the process can be targeted to zones of high risk or gassing sources at depth, e.g. old mine workings. Most grouting processes are relatively expensive. Grouted cut-offs or curtains can be installed in situations where other techniques involving excavation or displacement would be inappropriate. Cut-offs can be formed beneath existing structures, in or around services, and without disrupting surface traffic or the users of the services. Barry (1986) describes the installation of a grout curtain beneath a shallow passive venting trench (see Section 6.1) to provide an in-ground barrier to gas migration between the trench and an underlying low-permeability horizon. In this way the depth of the venting trench is effectively enhanced beyond its actual constructed depth.

Grouting is limited in its application by soil type. Variable soil types and fills containing high proportions of silts and fine sands or clays may not be amenable to treatment by a single type of grout; and a grouting programme based on the use of cement grouts, fine-ground cement grouts and chemical grouts may be required to achieve the desired results. As the grouting materials are dispersed within the soil mass they may be vulnerable to degradation by aggressive ground water or leachates and careful selection of grouting materials is required to ensure the long-term performance of a grouted zone.

Box 9 Grout injection of old mine workings

Raybould and Anderson (1987) describe the construction of a grout curtain to prevent methane migration from old abandoned mine workings and areas of landfill affecting nearby existing residential development. Methane gas was detected in and around residential properties in an area of St Helens. Gas levels ranged typically between 1% and 19% with carbon dioxide levels of between 1% to 12.5%. A grout curtain was established by grouting up the old mine workings along the boundary of the landfill site. The grout curtain was based on two rows of injection holes at 1.5 m centres, 1 m apart and staggered in plan. A grout mix of 6:1 pfa:cement was specified with the option of incorporating sand into the mix. Sulphate-resistant cement was also specified in view of the aggressive landfill environment. Other protective gas measures included passive ventilation of the landfill itself. Several months after the installation of the grout curtain and passive venting system no gas was detected in the vicinity of the affected properties.

By its very nature the use of grouting techniques to seal fissures and cracks in soils and rocks cannot be truly effective unless grout injection spacing is undertaken at very close centres and over a large area to prevent gas migration to surface. Staff *et al.* (1991) describe the use of injection grouting to seal leakage paths in fractured rock above disused coal mine workings as a protection measure to prevent methane ingress into existing residential properties. Despite these operations methane was still detected in properties indicating that the grouting undertaken had not been totally successful.

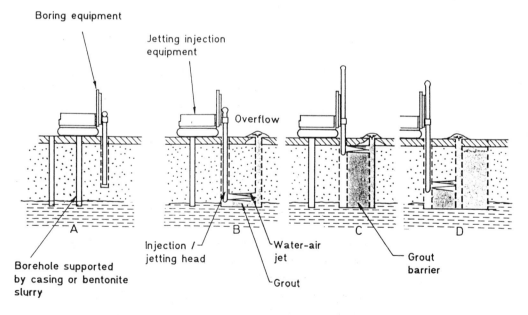

Figure 19 Principle of jet grouting to form in-ground barrier (after Childs, 1985)

Box 10 Grout injection to extend depth of in-ground clay

At Sandwell, a former industrial site has been redeveloped to provide land for a new school, allotments and public open space. Adjacent to the site was an old landfill facility where principally domestic and some industrial waste up to 10 m in depth, had been deposited during the 1960s and early 1970s. Methane concentrations within the landfill were recorded as high as 60% to 70% by volume in air with concentrations of carbon dioxide up to 30% by volume in air. As part of an overall gas-control system a venting trench together with an adjacent grout barrier were constructed together with the use of low-permeability gas membranes and passive ventilation to the school buildings. To prevent lateral gas migration the venting trench was constructed to intercept the groundwater table and was backfilled with 40-mm nominal sized granular material. The trench was excavated along the site boundary and is up to 7 m in depth capped with a subsurface layer of 40-mm nominal size stone filter material, connected to atmosphere by a shallow perimeter vent trench, and abutted on to an existing puddle clay cut-off trench. A section through the vent trench and in-ground barriers is shown below. An existing 5-m deep puddle clay cut-off trench was extended down to the underlying clay stratum by the use of a 3-m wide grouted gas barrier constructed directly below the puddle clay trench. Three rows of boreholes at 1-m centres, set out in a staggered pattern, were put down to provide injection points for the grout curtain. The outer two rows were injected with a pulverised fuel ash (pfa), cement and bentonite grout. The central row of boreholes directly beneath the puddle clay was grouted with pfa and bentonite only. The mix design varied between boreholes as site conditions dictated.

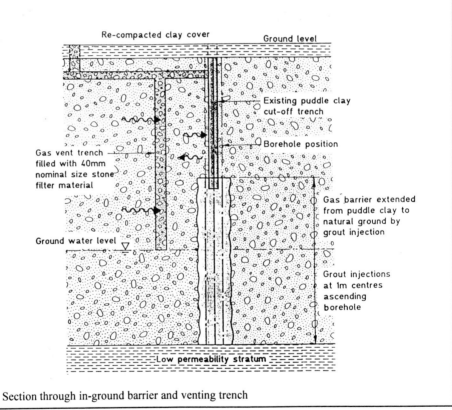

Section through in-ground barrier and venting trench

Jet grouting

This technique can be applied to the stabilisation of a much wider range of soils than can be grouted using pressure injection techniques. Jet grouting can be used to mix soils with a cement slurry in place to form a homogeneous mass of cement and soil. Alternatively, using a more sophisticated technique, the fine fraction of the soil, the fine sands, silts and clays, can be eroded by water and air jets and pushed to the surface, to be replaced by cement slurries injected into the ground. Vertical columns of jet grouted soil can be formed along the line of a proposed cut-off. Depending upon soil type, cut-offs up to 1.5 m thick can be formed in this way to depths of up to 15 m approximately (Childs, 1985). The principles of jet grouting are shown in Figure 19. The cost of the process is high. In addition, it is unlikely that competent jet grouted cut-offs could be formed in made ground or where there are obstructions interfering with the uniform formation of the jet grouted column. Chipp (1990) describes the use of a jet grouting technique to control landfill gas and leachate migration.

Vibrated beam wall

For this process an 'H' section steel pile is vibrated into the ground to the required depth and then extracted. During extraction a cement-based grout is injected at the toe of the pile. Each section is driven to overlap the preceding section to ensure complete coverage of the area. Figure 20 indicates the driving sequence, the extent of overlap, and the type of wall section achieved. The technique produces a relatively thin wall which is not ideal for gas control. However, a more secure barrier may be obtained if a double wall is installed with cross walls so as to form a system of independent cells (Jefferis, 1990). If pumped gas wells are installed in these cells as part of an in-ground active gas abstraction scheme, there is minimal potential for gas migration through the wall and the well flows can be used to monitor the performance of the system.

5.8   BARRIERS FORMED BY PILING TECHNIQUES

Barriers can be formed using conventional piling techniques. These can be either:

- driven sheet piles
- secant piles.

These types of piles and their use for in-ground gas protection are described below.

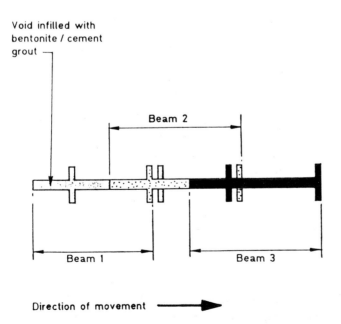

Figure 20 Vibrated beam in-ground barrier (after Childs, 1985)

Driven sheet piling

Driven sheet piles can be used to form continuous walls within soil to form an in-ground barrier. Driven steel or concrete elements may have applications in situations where barriers are required to provide both pollution control and provide some mechanical support to a substructure development. While conventional piling techniques might provide a partial barrier to gas migration the integrity of such walls, specifically in terms of their impermeability, cannot be relied upon. Walls formed from interlocking sheet piles are seldom totally waterproof and cannot, therefore, be considered totally gas proof. Other protective measures, such as in-ground venting, would inevitably have to be considered as part of an overall system to prevent gas migration (see Section 6.1). All these alternatives are relatively expensive and would only be considered in exceptional circumstances where other methods of construction were technically unacceptable.

Secant piling

This technique is often used in civil engineering to provide structural cut-off walls. The development of systems using 'soft' primary piles formed of bentonite/cement hardened slurry and concrete secondaries has allowed considerable cost savings in situations where a full wall of structural piles is not required. The installation sequence is shown in Figure 21. For gas protection there is always doubt regarding the joints between piles. Similar walls also can be formed by mix-in-place techniques for example using counter-rotating augers (Jefferis, 1990). Developments in this area are to be expected, though the range of suitable soil types may be rather limited. In general, secant piles walls are unlikely to be competitive as barriers unless there is a need for structural strength as well as low permeability to gas.

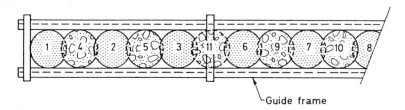

Guide frame

Pile numbers 1, 2, 3, 6, 7, 8, 'soft' primary piles

Pile numbers 4, 5, 11, 9, 10 'hard' secondary piles

Figure 21 Installation sequence for secant pile cut-off barrier (after Childs, 1985)

6   In-ground venting

The purpose of in-ground venting is to:

- reduce concentrations and emission rates of migrating gas from the ground
- encourage movement of gas in the ground away from development by forming a preferential path for gas to vent or be released to atmosphere at chosen locations away from sensitive areas of a site.

In the latter case, in-ground venting can itself provide a vertical or horizontal barrier to gas migration. However, because of variability in the permeability of surrounding ground, it cannot be guaranteed that gas would not continue to migrate beyond the ventilation system. For this reason, in-ground venting is best used to advantage in conjunction with an in-ground barrier system as described in Section 5.

6.1   PASSIVE IN-GROUND VENTING

Passive in-ground venting is the controlled release and dispersal of gas from the ground to atmosphere *via* a preferential path and special surface outlets.

Dilution and dispersion of the gas occurs at the outlet or point of release into the surrounding atmosphere. For passive in-ground venting to be successful it should be designed and constructed to allow gas migration to occur at all times, irrespective of fluctuations in concentration or the emission rate of the gas or changes in ambient atmospheric conditions, i.e. wind speed, temperature, barometric pressure and rainfall. This requires detailed knowledge of these variable parameters so that the venting system can be designed confidently. Comprehensive site investigation and gas monitoring data will be required. Raybould *et al* (1995) give guidance on the requirements and procedures for the investigation and monitoring of gassing sites.

6.1.1   Principles of design

Passive in-ground venting is based on the principle that gas is allowed to migrate and disperse to the atmosphere from the ground by the processes of diffusion and advection. These processes are described in Section 3.3.3. Within an in-ground passive venting system molecular diffusion is the dominant migration process where the gas concentration is high and the pressure gradient is low. Conversely migration by advection will be dominant when the concentration is low and the pressure gradient is high.

The venting system should be highly permeable relative to the surrounding ground and offer minimum resistance to gas migration. Careful assessment of the gassing regime in terms of gas concentration and emission rate is therefore essential in order to design a passive in-ground venting system which will be successful in diluting gas concentrations and dispersing the gas to atmosphere. Where high gas concentrations and/or high emission rates exist, passive in-ground venting may prove inadequate as a method to disperse gas in a controlled and safe manner. In these circumstances active abstraction can be used (see Section 6.2).

Table 17 Advantages and disadvantages of passive in-ground venting

Advantages	Disadvantages
Relatively rapid simple construction.	May be ineffective where high gas concentrations and emission rates are encountered.
Relatively low cost.	Gas emission from the vent may give rise to odour nuisance.
Low maintenance.	Open vents at ground surface can become 'clogged' or blocked with intrusion of surrounding soil or micro-organisms or groundwater.
Usually remains effective for a long time.	Effectiveness influenced by the permeability to gas of the surrounding ground.
Can be installed with minimal intrusion within a development.	Installation of passive venting systems in gassing ground will require safe disposal of excavation spoil (see Section 4.2).

6.1.1   Methods of installation and applications

Passive in-ground venting can be installed by the use of:

- venting trenches
- venting wells
- drainage layers.

These types of installations are described below.

Venting trenches

Venting trenches, also known as gas-permeable trenches, are probably the most frequently used method of passive in-ground venting. The trench is constructed using conventional excavating plant sufficiently deep to intercept the lowest possible layer through which gas may migrate and is keyed into an underlying low-permeability stratum. The trench is then backfilled with a granular material of high permeability to gas relative to the surrounding ground, e.g. natural aggregate, crushed concrete or broken brick. Granular material ranging in size from 20 to 150 mm has been used, but the actual sizing should be selected in relation to the particle size distribution of the surrounding soil in order to minimise ingress of fines (i.e. clay, silt and sand) which can clog the backfill and impair gas migration. An alternative solution to prevent ingress of fines is to surround the backfill in a geotextile filter material. Venting trenches have proved effective as a gas-protection measure to both existing and new development. Several case studies have been reported where granular-filled venting trenches have been used in conjunction with an in-ground synthetic barrier (see also Section 5.5) in order to control gas migration and to reduce high concentrations of methane and carbon dioxide to safe acceptable levels on new and existing developments (e.g. Card and Roche, 1991; CSS, 1987 and Parker, 1986). Examples of venting trenches are shown in Figure 22. Other examples of venting trenches combined with in-ground barriers are described in Box 24.

In circumstances where the reach of normal excavating equipment is insufficient for the required depth of a venting trench, e.g. 5 to 8 m, other techniques have been used to provide gas protection. These include deep gas wells and grout injection (Section 5.7). Jeffcris (1990) describes the construction of deep permeable walls to control gas migration. The installation is similar to the construction of a slurry trench cut-off barrier as described in Section 5.6. However, in these circumstances the drainage wall is formed by excavating a trench under a degradeable polymer slurry for trench stability. On completion of excavation the trench is backfilled with a gravel drainage material and the slurry broken down with an oxidising agent or left to degrade naturally to form a permeable venting trench.

Another more recent development is the construction of a venting trench or venting zone using compressed air to break up or fracture the ground. In trials undertaken on gassing ground, methane concentrations were reported to have been reduced by 50% using this technique. Some concern has been expressed at the dangers of pumping air into methane gassing ground, particularly in coal mining areas creating explosive conditions.

In theory, in order to maximise the dispersion efficiency of the venting trench the granular backfill should be left exposed at ground surface. In this way the process of molecular diffusion and advection acting in the trench can be maximised. However the disadvantages of an exposed trench are that:

- the granular surface may easily become 'clogged' with wind-blown soil or waste, fine soil or weeds, reducing the dispersion efficiency: under these circumstances methane may accumulate in the trench creating an explosive hazard

- emissions of gas, particularly landfill gas, may create an odour problem in the vicinity of the trench, and may thus be a nuisance to the general public (see Section 2.5.3)

- high methane emissions may give rise to explosive/flammable mixtures which may be ignited by naked flames and thus be a risk to the general public

- the open trench can act as a land drain and become waterlogged, thus impairing its function.

To some extent these disadvantages can be overcome by regular maintenance to prevent 'clogging' of the granular surface, siting of open trenches in development protected from the general public and incorporating adequate drainage measures into the trench. Drainage measures include:

- a positive piped drainage system laid to hydraulic gradients

- design of the trench to act as a soakaway to surface water infiltration. Guidance on the design of soakaways is given in BRE Digest 365 (BRE,1991b).

Where venting trenches cannot be located away from the general public, it is usual practice to design ventilation trenches with a covered surface within a development environment, (see Figure 22). Controlled dispersion of gas occurs at chosen locations *via* vent stacks or chimneys set into the trench. In this way the disadvantages of open trenches as mentioned above may be overcome. However, it should be borne in mind that the efficiency of a covered venting trench to disperse gas by advection will be significantly reduced. This is because under these circumstances gas dispersion by diffusion will be the dominant, if not the only, process acting. Surface reinstatement, incorporation of pipework, and specific venting arrangements will significantly increase resistance to gas flow by advection and thus reduce the pressure gradient in the venting system.

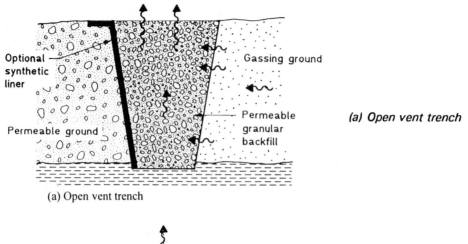

(a) Open vent trench

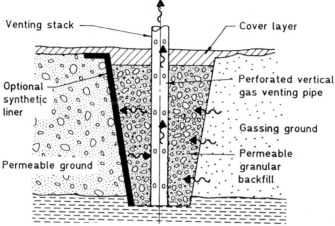

(b) Simple closed trench with vent stack

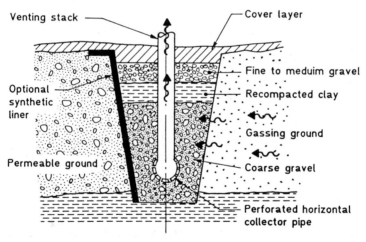

(c) Closed trench with recompacted clay cover and surface drainage layer

Figure 22 Examples of venting trenches

Surface reinstatement with compacted clay together with a geotextile filter will prevent
both surface water infiltration and clogging. Horizontally laid perforated or slotted
collector pipes should be installed in the trench and connected to the surface vent pipes.
The purpose of these collector pipes is to act as a preferential pathway within the
granular backfill for gas to migrate to the vent stack, either by diffusion or advection *via*
the pipework even if the granular backfill becomes clogged or impaired due to in-
service failure. The pipework can be rodded and kept free as a preferential pathway for

gas (a series of rodding chambers should be incorporated into the pipework runs). Futhermore, the installation of pipework allows the passive venting trench to be uprated to an active abstraction system at any time in the future if the gassing regime significantly increases beyond the capacity of the passive system (see Section 6.2).

Collector pipes of 100 to 200 mm diameter have been used. They should be designed not to be crushed under the weight of overburden granular backfill in the trench. In trenches deeper than (say 1.5 to 2 m) the overburden pressure can become significant on a buried pipe. All pipework should be laid to hydraulic falls and rise to the locations of vent stacks. Guidance on the design of buried pipes is given in Young and O'Reilly (1983) and WRc (1990). General guidance on the design of drainage for building development is given in BS 8301:1985. The most widely used pipe drainage material is HDPE although other plastic materials have been used, e.g. LDPE, uPVC. In cold weather uPVC pipes can become brittle and crack and this may limit their use in shallow trench systems where their durability may be reduced in frozen ground. Vitrified clay pipes have also been used.

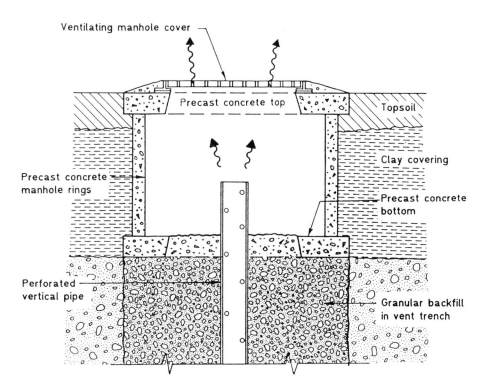

Figure 23 General arrangement of venting manhole

Small diameter gas wells, e.g. 150 to 200 mm, can be installed using conventional cable percussion boring techniques. They are usually lined using slotted or perforated plastic pipe (i.e. HDPE pipework) surrounded by granular fill. Depending on the particle size distribution of the surrounding ground a fabric filter may also be needed to prevent entry of fines and clogging of the well. Prefabricated vertical drains or sandwick drains can also be used to increase the permeability of the ground in the vertical direction thus allowing gas to be vented to atmosphere. Guidance on the design and performance of vertical band drains is given by Holtz et al.(1991).

Large-diameter gas wells can be installed using augered or driven piling techniques with the open bore backfilled with granular material instead of concrete. Augered wells can be installed in ground which is stable enough to remain open. An open shaft is formed with a rotary auger which is then backfilled with granular material to form the gas well. Typically, augered wells can be installed up to 1 m in diameter. Gas wells can also be constructed using driven shell piles. The gas well is installed by threading perforated/slotted concrete on to a steel mandrel and driving the shells to depths of typically between 10 and 20 m. The system utilises high-strength cylindrical concrete sections to build up a well shaft. A high-strength pointed shoe assists penetration of the well shaft through difficult ground, e.g. made ground, landfill. Wells of 340 mm, 400 mm and 530 mm nominal external diameter can be installed.

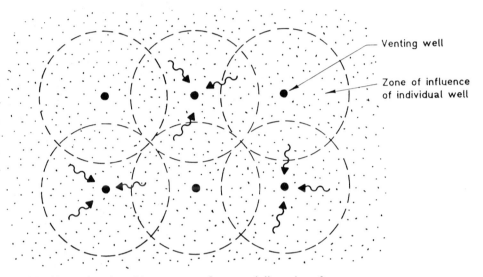

(a) Random or regular grid arrangement for general dispersion of gas

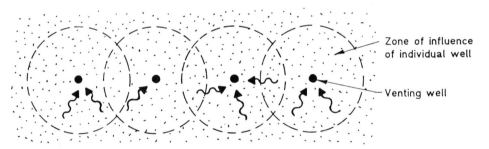

(b) Regular arrangement to form in-ground venting barrier to resist gas migration

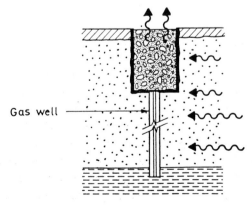

(c) Use of gas well to increase effective depth of ventilation trench

Figure 24 Applications of gas venting wells

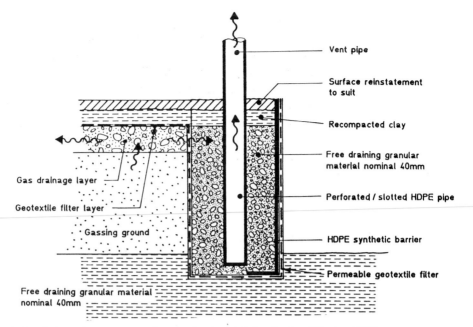

(a) Gas drainage layer connected to venting trench (after Card and Roche, 1991)

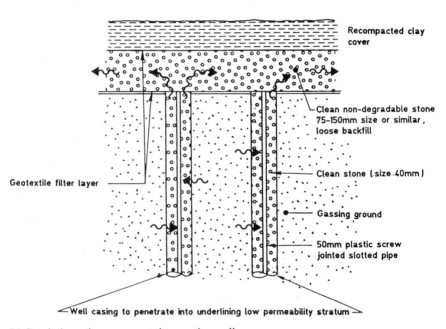

(b) Gas drainage layer connected to venting wells

Figure 25 Use of gas drainage layers

Stone columns formed of compacted granular material (typically 20 to 75 mm in size) can act as ventilation wells in low-permeability soils. They can be installed using conventional vibro-replacement techniques to depths of up to 15 to 20 m. Greenwood and Thomson (1984) and Leach and Goodger (1991) give general technical guidance on the design and construction of stone columns. The diameter of the columns can range between 300 to 750 mm depending on ground conditions. Large wells are usually unlined although ingress of fines from the surrounding soil can take place the effect of clogging and impairment on venting of gas is unlikely to be significant given their relatively large diameter.

The principles of design of a gas well are similar to those for the venting trench. However, there is a fundamental difficulty in estimating the zone of influence of an individual venting well and this gives rise to uncertainty of well spacings. The zone of influence will be affected by the permeability of the ground, groundwater levels, ground disturbance and gas generation rates. In addition, the zone of influence can also be affected by the design of the gas well including number, spacing and frequency, diameter, roughness of perforations and grading of granular filter. Parker (1986) considers that a well spacing of 25 to 50 m is adequate to ensure sufficient overlap of influence zones. Attempts have been made to correlate gas flow measurements in gas wells with the zone of influence in conjunction with landfill gas abstraction (see Section 6.2) but these have been largely unsuccessful. Given the difficulty, therefore, of estimating the sphere of influence in any given ground (as shown in Figure 24b and c) the use of gas wells should not be relied upon as acting as a barrier to gas migration. A continuous venting trench and/or in-ground barrier should be used.

Drainage layers

This is a layer of granular material which is placed to form a gas-permeable horizon beneath a horizontal in-ground barrier such as clay or a synthetic liner (see Sections 5.4 and 5.5). The purpose of the drainage layer is to prevent accumulation of gas and build-up of pressure acting on the underside of a low-permeability barrier. In this way gas is encouraged to migrate laterally where it can be allowed to disperse to atmosphere at specific locations *via* a venting trench arrangement.

A variation of the drainage layer is a gas drain which consists of a shallow trench typically 1 m deep constructed from granular material. Drainage layers or gas drains interconnected to venting trenches or wells are installed as part of current landfill engineering practice to provide an additional preferential pathway for gas to move laterally within the waste to gas wells. Gas drainage layers are also used as cover layers in conjunction with the redevelopment of contaminated land not only as a protection measure against uncontrolled gas migration but to provide capillary break layers to guard against soil-suction induced contamination (Leach and Goodger, 1991).

In all applications the drainage layer or gas drain has to be combined with a venting trench or venting well to ensure controlled dispersion of gases to atmosphere. Drainage layers have been used successfully for development on areas of old landfill and where the site surface is of low permeability. Roche and Card (1991) describe the construction of a venting layer beneath domestic gardens and areas of hardstanding to prevent accumulation of methane. Typical details of drainage layer construction combined with venting trenches are shown in Figure 25. As with the other methods of passive in-ground venting, the incorporation of collector pipes within the drainage layer can assist gas migration, reduce maintenance and extend service life.

6.2   ACTIVE IN-GROUND ABSTRACTION

Mechanical pumping of gas from a collection system comprising perforated pipework laid on or in the ground is known as active abstraction or gas pumping. Active abstraction differs from passive in-ground venting in that dilution and dispersion of gas occurs by mechanical pumping to induce a pressure gradient in the venting system. The collected gas is either vented and released to atmosphere at a specific location *via* a vent stack (see Section 6.1.2) or flared off if the abstracted gas is potentially combustible. Active abstraction is most effective in situations of high and variable gas concentrations and/or rates of emission, which cannot be dispersed in a controlled manner by passive in-ground venting which relies on the process of diffusion and advection in the natural environment (see Section 6.1). Active abstraction is a technique used in current landfill engineering practice either to disperse gas safely to atmosphere or to burn for power generation.

6.2.1 Principles of design

As outlined above, gas dilution and dispersion from the ground to atmosphere is achieved by creating a pressure gradient from mechanical pumping.

The design of an active abstraction scheme relies upon estimation of the likely gas yield and duration, based upon information regarding the gas concentration, emission rate and nature and volume of gassing material. This requires detailed site investigation together with gas monitoring data to evaluate the gas regime. Even so it is often necessary to undertake a site pumping trial to be able to determine such parameters as:

- mechanical pump capacity
- the zone of abstraction of individual gas wells
- spacing of gas wells.

Mechanical pumping creates suction which draws gas through the abstraction system to the point of venting. The effect of pumping is to create a negative pressure gradient in the surrounding ground. This pressure gradient can vary significantly. The effective zone of abstraction in gassing ground surrounding a perforated collector pipe has been measured at up to 30 to 50 m (Baker, 1987 and Campbell, 1987). This effectiveness, however, depends on a number of factors such as:

- the magnitude of the suction (nominal suction of 5 millibars at gas well head is usually required)
- the permeability of the ground from which gas is to be abstracted
- the permeability of the surface cover
- the presence of groundwater limiting the zone of suction.

The provision of perforated collector pipes within a granular medium can greatly improve the efficiency of the pumping system because they not only intercept laterally migrating gases but also offer less resistance to pumping. However, it is important that air is not drawn into the system from the ground surface as this can result in:

- loss in suction and effectiveness of the abstraction system
- air being drawn into the abstraction system which in the presence of methane may give rise to a flammable gas mixture and the potential risk of explosion within the system or the ground itself.

For this reason the abstraction system should be as airtight as possible. All pipework which is installed in trenches, wells or layers has to be covered with a low-permeability material, e.g. natural clay or soil/bentonite. In this regard the construction of an active abstraction system is similar to that for passive venting trenches which are closed and vented at specific locations (see Section 6.1.2). Indeed passive venting system should be designed in such a way that active abstraction of gas can be undertaken, if gas generation significantly increases for whatever reason.

6.2.2 Installation components

General guidance on the plant and equipment necessary for an active abstraction system are given by the DoE (1986, 1991). Gas monitoring and maintenance of the components of an active abstraction scheme is essential if effective control is required without interruption due to breakdown or failure. This aspect has to be considered in the overall design of a scheme and will require the following:

- provision for servicing and maintenance during the effective lifetime of the development
- provision of secondary protection measures to the development to provide gas protection during periods of 'down time' for servicing or if the system fails
- built-in gas monitoring and alarm facilities to warn of adverse conditions in the system
- provision of long-term management facilities to maintain and service the system and respond to alarms when triggered (see Section 13).

These factors should be included in the overall costs when considering active in-ground abstraction compared with other protection measures. The major components to be considered are as follows:

- gas collection systems
- venting arrangement/flare stack
- gas pumping plant.

These components are described below.

Gas collection system

Most abstraction systems comprise extraction wells linked by trenches or horizontal drainage layers (see Section 6.1.2). Extraction wells are constructed using conventional cable percussion boring techniques usually below the depth of gassing ground and keyed into an underlying low-permeability stratum. Extraction wells are constructed usually with a diameter of between 0.3 and 1 m. The well pipe, usually some 100 to 150 mm in diameter, perforated except for the top few metres, is inserted into the drilled hole. The annulus is backfilled with permeable material such as gravel, rock or broken bricks, and is capped by a layer of impermeable material such as clay or bentonite/cement. The head of each well may be fitted with a flow/pressure control valve and suitable monitoring points for flow rate, pressure and temperature measurements if required. These measurements may be particularly important in a gas-migration control system. In some installations, individual wells are linked to a central manifold where the measurement and control devices may be positioned. A typical arrangement of a gas abstraction well is shown in Figure 26. Where abstraction wells will not be permanent structures they may be constructed of either plastic or steel. Permanent extraction wells should preferably be constructed using a plastic such as HDPE or uPVC, depending on other factors such as ground conditions, contamination, and leachate levels.

Abstraction wells should be joined together by plastic pipe, usually of at least 100 mm diameter, which is in turn connected to a mechanical suction pump. These pipes, which can be laid on the surface of the site or buried, should be sloped or designed so as to facilitate the drainage of condensate back to the well or to a sump for its removal. It is important that no other traps or low spots are present in this pipework. The use of metal pipes in either vertical or horizontal gas collection lines is not recommended as they may corrode. The plasticiser in some plastic pipes can react with ultra-violet light, causing embrittlement, and some grades of uPVC are susceptible to softening (and hence collapse) at temperatures above 45° which frequently can be reached in a landfill environment. In addition, uPVC can become brittle in cold weather particularly in frozen ground.

Venting arrangement/flare stack

The usual method of disposal of abstracted gas is to burn it at a flarestack. This is the preferred safe method of disposal of abstracted gas. In addition, odour from gas can be effectively removed by flaring (see Section 2.5.3). Current government policy in the UK is to encourage flaring of abstracted gases (methane and carbon dioxide) to the atmosphere thus reducing their contribution to global warming effects.

All flarestacks need to be properly safeguarded to prevent the possible occurrence of an explosion within the abstraction system. A flame arrester is an essential component between a pump and a flare stack. Experience indicates that regular maintenance of flame arresters is essential because of clogging by sand, dust and water. Correct flame temperature is vital to ensure all gas constituents are burnt. For landfill gas, minor constituents can pose a health risk if not totally burnt (see Section 2.5.3). Typically the temperature of the gas at the flarestack should be in excess of 1100°C.

On most gassing sites selected for building development, the gas regime may be such that the rate of supply or concentration of gas is insufficient to support combustion. In these circumstances support fuel may be needed to burn the gas.

Gas pumping plant

The main items comprising the gas pumping plant are usually a gas moisture removal trap, an extractor pump, associated pipework, valves, control and monitoring equipment, power supplies and, possibly, a gas cooler. In addition, a flare stack may be required. An important plant item is some form of moisture knockout trap or chiller unit. The efficiency required of such a trap and its position within the plant will depend on the pump being used. Such traps also may be required within the gas collection system in the landfill and should be designed to be safe from implosion under negative pressure and contain adequate drain-off facilities which will avoid air intrusion during operation. The distribution network of pipes and controls required at each site will be unique. At some sites consideration can also be given to converting the combustible gases into electrical power. This is particularly the case where abstraction systems are established to control landfill gas migration. Such plants may need substantial electrical sub-stations, protected from gas ingress, to provide connection to the National Grid.

Box 11 Active abstraction for protection to new development

Stearns and Petoyan (1984) describe several development projects in California, USA, where active abstraction was used to protect new development built over landfill. One of these projects, a 10.5-ha ,15-m deep landfill site, comprising household and commercial waste, has been developed as a drive-in theatre. The active abstraction system comprised 30 gas wells for on-site protection and 19 perimeter gas wells for off-site migration control. Abstracted gas was continuously flared. The system was designed to maintain methane concentrations at ground surface at less than 50% LEL. Other protection measures include a low-permeability membrane within the ground slab of the main building together with an automatic gas-detection system within the building.

6.2.3 Applications

As a technique to control gas migration, active in-ground abstraction is very effective. It has particular advantages where gas generation and migration are particularly widespread and would be difficult to contain using in-ground barriers and passive venting techniques. Abstraction is particularly suited to controlling gas migration from closed landfill sites and mine workings which affect general development (Creedy, 1991).

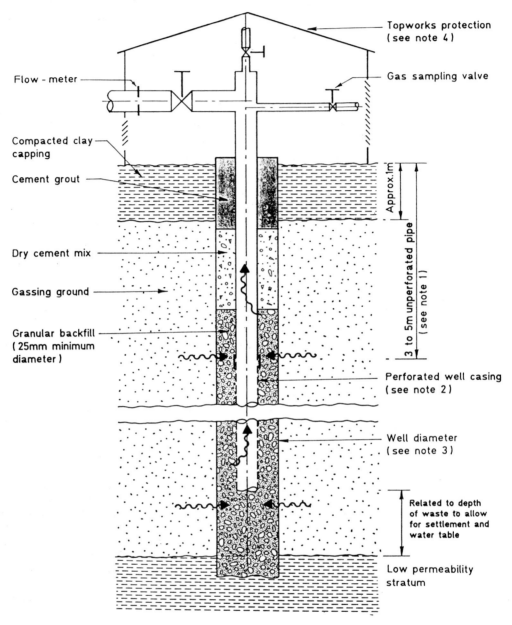

Notes:

1. Upper 3 to 5 m of pipe should be unperforated, the exact length depending on the depth of the gassing ground and the height of the water/leachate table within the waste.

2. The remaining pipe should be perforated (approx. 20% perforated area) preferably made of uPVC, HDPE or polypropylene and of at least 110 mm diameter.

3. Overall well diameter depends on the amount of landfill gas to be extracted from the well. This should be determined by static tests on trial wells and in most circumstances should preferably be a minimum of 300 mm diameter.

4. Topworks may be suitably protected above ground by a robust ventilated enclosure or, below ground, in a manhole which does not compromise the integrity of the compacted clay capping.

Figure 26   General arrangement of gas abstraction well (after Waste Management Paper No 27: DoE, 1991)

Active abstraction has been used widely to protect existing development, particularly in inner city areas, from gas migration from closed landfill sites and abandoned shallow mine workings (Parker, 1986; Campbell, 1987 and Ashton, 1991). The reasons for choosing this method include:

- the gassing source cannot be specifically located and the nature of the gas identified, thus future trends in the gas regime cannot be predicted with certainty

- widespread gas migration affecting large areas of existing development makes containment by in-ground barriers or passive in-ground ventilation techniques impracticable.

The design of an active in-ground abstraction system should be able to accommodate changes with time not only in the gas regime but also in the surrounding environment. There is also some evidence that gas abstraction may accelerate degradation of organic material resulting in increased ground settlement (Ashton, 1991). Differential settlement of gassing fills can result in rupture of pipework and failure of gas collection systems. Box 12 describes a case study where gas abstraction affected the gas regime itself.

Groundwater can also have other deleterious effects particularly where pollutants from contaminated land are present. The presence of groundwater limits the zone of gas abstraction. If water or other fluid enters the collection system it can reduce the suction in the system, corrode the mechanical plant, and lead to eventual failure. Water/leachate is believed to have been partly the cause of failure of the active abstraction scheme at the Liverpool Garden Festival site (Couth, 1990). The scheme had failed after six years service because of a combination of differential settlement of the gas collection system buried within the former landfill and leachate corroding steel pipework and mechanical components.

Box 12 Active abstraction for protection to existing development

At a site near Ashton-under-Lyne, an active gas abstraction scheme had been installed to control landfill gas migration from a closed landfill, some 8 ha in area, affecting adjoining residential properties and where methane concentrations within one building were found to be greater than 1% by volume in air. The scheme initially comprised 60 perimeter gas wells at 20 m centres, all linked by pipework laid in trenches to a flare stack via a pump unit. The pump flare unit operated at about 25% methane content with a total flow rate of approximately 100 m³/h. Initially the scheme was effective in reducing methane to non-detectable levels in the surrounding houses. However, after 9 months of continual service, gas levels began to rise again requiring further gas abstraction wells to be installed over the site area. The reason for the sudden increase in gas levels is unclear, but it is believed that changes in the groundwater level were affected by the abstraction system which, in turn, altered the anaerobic/aerobic condition of the landfill, causing renewed generation of methane.

It is possible to collect and abstract gas from a passive in-ground venting system providing all points of gas venting direct to atmosphere are sealed to prevent air ingress. Active abstraction can be provided also using portable abstraction equipment which can be brought to site and installed in a relatively short period of time, to provide temporary protection until more permanent measures have been designed and constructed. An example of portable gas abstraction equipment is shown in Figure 27. A portable active abstraction system has been used on this basis at a site near Exmouth in Devon to protect existing residential development surrounding an area of gassing landfill (Roche and Card, 1991).

Figure 27 Example of portable active abstraction and flaring plant

The main advantages and disadvantages of active in-ground abstraction are summarised in Table 18.

A further limitation of active abstraction is that under equilibrium conditions abstracted gases are replaced by further gas (drawn to the area by the abstraction flow pattern) to maintain continuity of flow. Where abstraction rates exceed the generation or emission rate of the gas at source, air can be drawn preferentially from the surface. Therefore where new or existing development is constructed directly over the gassing source it is possible that gas concentrations may remain unchanged until either the gas generation in the ground is totally exhausted or gas abstraction exceeds gas production in which case air may be drawn into the ground and could give rise to flammable mixtures. A technique used to achieve simultaneous gas abstraction and replacement by injection of inert gases is described by Manley *et al.*(1991). This technique is described more fully in Section 11 in the context of protection to existing development.

An adaptation of active in-ground abstraction is active in-ground venting (also called active soil venting). This technique has been used widely in North America and Northern Europe to protect development including subsurface development from the migration of methane and associated hazards, VOCs and radon. Active in-ground venting is essentially the reverse of active abstraction. A positive pressure relative to atmosphere and the ground is induced at the abstraction gas well. The induced pressure gradient reverses the direction of gas flows and this has been used to protect development by creating a zone of higher pressure beneath buildings and subsurface development (see also Section 12.3). The principle of the technique is shown in Figure 57. However, as in the case of using compressed air to form passive in-ground venting trenches (see Section 6.1.2) there is concern in the UK of the dangers of pumping air into gassing ground, particularly where explosive conditions may be created with a source of methane, e.g. old landfill sites, or ground above old mine workings.

Table 18 Advantages and disadvantages of active in-ground abstraction

Advantages	Disadvantages
Very effective in rapidly reducing gas levels once the system has been commissioned and is operating.	Can take a long time to design and install.
Can be effective to control high gas concentrations and emission rates.	The design requires detailed knowledge of ground conditions, nature and volume of gassing material, as well as reliable measurements of in-ground gas concentrations and emissions rates, and estimation of worst credible gas levels.
Collected gas can be flared, thus no noxious or hazardous gases released to atmosphere.	Trial abstraction system nearly always required to prove design.
Collected gas can be utilised for power generation if high in methane, which can offset costs of system installation. Flexibility in design means it can be used on most sites and terrain.	Effectiveness of abstraction limited by the presence of groundwater.
Portable abstraction equipment can be used to reduce the gas regime in the short-term.	High level of maintenance required to minimise down time.
Flexibility in design means it can be used on most sites and terrain.	Rarely adequate as sole means of protection to development.

7   Venting for buildings

7.1   PASSIVE VENTING FOR BUILDINGS

Passive venting, also called natural venting, to buildings or structures can be defined as the movement of air through openings in the building or structure fabric by the action of natural climatic conditions. For this reason passive venting is suitable in situations where precise control over the air quality and volume flow rate of fresh air is not critical to dilute gas concentrations to safe acceptable levels.

Where adequate dilution cannot be achieved, other protection measures have to be considered either to replace or supplement a passive venting system. In the particular case of methane accumulation, active venting will normally be the only safe and acceptable alternative technique (see Section 7.2). This means that a detailed assessment of the gas concentration of individual components and surface emission rate is vital to enable the correct choice between passive and active venting to be made. In the absence of reliable gas monitoring information it is good practice to assume that active venting is required for gas protection until proven otherwise. The conceptual design of gas protection measures in relation to the nature of gas and type of development is discussed in Section 3.2.

In a similar manner to passive in-ground venting, passive venting for buildings relies on the principle of dilution and dispersion to control the ingress of methane and associated gases by the processes of gas diffusion and advection (see Sections 6.1 and 3.3.3). However, beneath or within the confined space of a building gas diffusion can be extremely slow and generally cannot be relied upon to provide adequate dilution and dispersion. For this reason passive venting for buildings is usually designed on the basis of advection and the application of a pressure gradient to cause gas dilution and dispersion (see Section 3.3.3). In this context the principle of passive venting to buildings can be summarised as shown in Figure 28. An adequate volume flow rate of fresh air, Q, is provided to dilute a gas contaminant entering a ventilated space at a rate of ingress, q, to a safe acceptable equilibrium design concentration, c_e. Design concentrations appropriate for the range of gases associated with methane are discussed in Section 2.5.5.

Passive venting to development affected by methane and associated gases can be applied in two ways:

- dilution of gas within the building fabric by providing adequate volume flow rate of fresh air to disperse gas
- dilution of gas before entering the building, i.e. reducing the concentration to safe acceptable levels so that ingress of gas into the building fabric, if any, will have no adverse effect.

Adequate fresh air ventilation is an essential requirement within a habitable building or structure. In the UK, guidance and design methods on the principles of natural ventilation are provided in the following documents:

- British Standard BS 5925:1991 and CIBSE Guide Volume A4 (CIBSE, 1986)

- Building Research Establishment Digests Nos 206 (BRE, 1977) and 210 (BRE, 1978) which give guidance on estimating dilution and dispersion of gas based on natural ventilation principles.

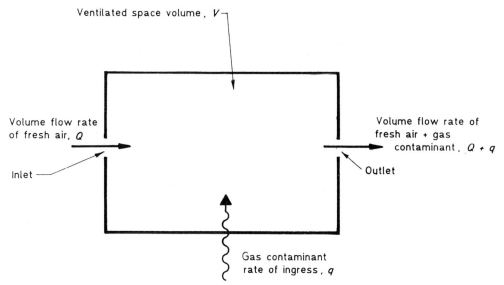

From BS 5925:1991 assuming incoming fresh air is free of gas contaminant the concentration, c, of a gas contaminant introduced at constant rate, q, after time, t, into a ventilated volume, V, is given by

$$V = c = \left[\frac{1}{1 + Q/q}\right] \left[(1-e^{-(1+Q/q)(qt/v)}\right]$$

As t increases the concentration reaches an equilibrium value, c_e given by

$$c_e = \left[\frac{q}{Q + q}\right]$$

Figure 28 Gas contaminant entering a ventilated space

Advice given in these documents allows a designer to provide adequate ventilation to any building development for habitable purposes. All habitable buildings have a capacity to dilute any ingress of gas, thus providing a margin of safety. Risk will arise if:

- there is a confined space in the building which is inadequately ventilated
- the rate of ingress of gas is sufficiently high to render dilution and dispersion by natural ventilation inadequate.

Given the inherent difficulties of being able to measure and predict gas levels with any certainty (see Section 2.5.5), it is best practice to endeavour to dilute the gas before it can enter the building. This is achieved by providing passive venting between the building and the underlying ground to dilute and disperse any emission of gas.

7.1.1   Principles of design

To achieve passive venting a void is formed between the building and underlying ground. The void is connected to the external envelope of the building by vents. The principle of passive venting beneath a building is illustrated in Figure 29. It should be noted that where the surface emission rate, q, is from a combination of gaseous contaminants, e.g. methane, carbon dioxide and other associated gases, then the required volume flow rate of fresh air, Q, should be calculated on the basis of the individual emission rate for each gas component. A fundamental problem in designing a passive venting system arises in quantifying the parameters:

- concentration, c, of each gas component entering the void space
- surface emission rate into the void space, q, of each gas component.

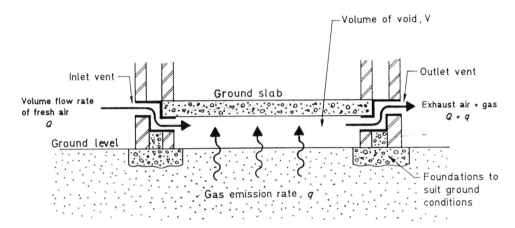

From BS 5925: 1991, Q, is given by the formula

$$Q = q \left[\frac{100 - C_e}{C_e} \right]$$

where q = the surface emission rate of the particular gas contaminant into the void

c_e = the concentration of the gas contaminant at equilibrium, i.e. the designed safe acceptable concentration.

Figure 29 Principle of passive venting beneath a building

These parameters have to be based on the results of gas monitoring. Thus, the quality and extent of the gas monitoring data greatly influence design and the reliability and effectiveness of the installed protection measure. Measuring of surface emission rate and interpreting the measurements for design requires considerable judgement. Current techniques of estimating surface emission rate are based on:

- direct measurement including volume flow and flow velocity of gas from the ground *via* a borehole or standpipe
- indirect measurement based on assessment of total volume of gas at source and soil permeability to gas: from this the volume flow rate of gas likely to be emitted at surface is estimated.

Further information on emission rate measurement and interpretation is given by Pecksen (1986), Crowhurst (1987), Crowhurst and Manchester (1993) and Raybould *et al* (1995).

Further problems arise because the methods of measuring gas concentration, c, and surface emission rate, q, cannot take account of future trends in the gassing regime. Measured gas parameters at the time of any investigation might not reflect conditions during the life of the development. For this reason, gas parameters (i.e. concentration and emission rate) used in the design of gas protection measures should take acco. these possible variations (see Section 2.5.5).

In those situations where there is a risk of an accumulation of gas which might lead to an explosion, the Building Regulations Approved Document C4 (DoE, 1992) requires ventilation to a void beneath a floor slab (timber or concrete) to be provided by wall openings equivalent to 1500 mm² for each metre run of wall. Currently, however, there is, no quantitative design method to calculate the actual venting requirements of an underfloor void which will provide the required volume flow rate of fresh air to dilute gas of known concentration and emission rate. Most practitioners/designers base their designs on the methods set down in BS 5925:1991 and/or CIBSE (1986) which are strictly for providing ventilation to buildings or superstructures of normal room size dimensions. These documents allow the designer to determine the required number, size and spacing of air vents for given environmental and climatic conditions surrounding the building/development.

Notwithstanding the difficulties of design, work reported by Carpenter et al.(1985) and Pecksen (1986) demonstrated good agreement between experimentally and theoretically derived volume flow rates of fresh air based on the accepted methods for designing natural ventilation for buildings. As a general rule the theoretical air flow rates were found to be slightly higher than the actual required air flow rates based on experimental evidence. This may in part be because of cross-wall ventilation between vents increasing actual air-flow rates. The experimental work was carried out in conjunction with full-sized test rigs set up to model ventilation beneath a floor area of 44.3 m² in an underfloor void of variable volume constructed over gassing ground. The results of this work were used as the basis of gas protection design to development in London Docklands (Carpenter, 1988). Methane concentrations of up to 20% to 30% by volume in air were identified with the majority of surface emission rates less than 0.01 m/s. From these data and experimental trials it was established that passive venting, using an open underslab void of height 225 mm with 50% side area of the void ventilated to atmosphere using wall ventilators, could be employed. Based on the above evidence for buildings of small plan area there is some justification to use the accepted theory of natural ventilation for buildings as outlined in BS 5925:1991 and CIBSE (1986).

For buildings with large ground floor areas and thus potentially large voids it is not feasible to construct a ground slab with a single open void under its entire area. These buildings are likely to have internal downstanding beams or foundations which subdivide the void space restricting the position of external vents and making it difficult to ventilate adequately. This may be overcome by incorporating vents or ducts in internal downstanding beams to allow cross ventilation. However, the design and layout of internal vents can be restricted by statutory or local requirements for fire precautions and ventilation. Reference should be made to BS 5588:1991 and also the Building Regulations Approved Document C4 (DoE, 1992) for guidance. The requirements for ventilation in the event of a fire, may on occasion, be incompatible with requirements for passive venting beneath a building and this may limit its use as a protection measure in certain situations.

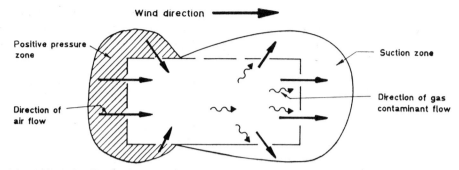

(a) Action of wall vent. On an isolated building wind forces exert pressures greater than current atmospheric pressure on its windward side and lower pressures on its leeward side creating suction. Increasing the number of wall vents will enhance cross-wall ventilation

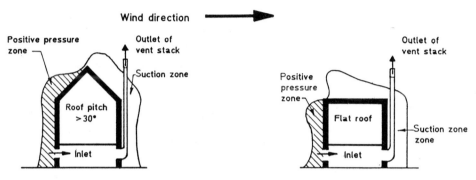

(b) Wind pressure and suction zones. Vent stacks can be used to enhance ventilation in the underslab void. The pressure zones at roof level need to be assessed for all wind directions on the building. Suction at the vent stack will generally be increased for taller buildings

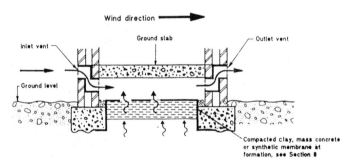

(c) Use of in-ground barriers to reduce gas emission rate into underfloor void

Figure 30 Methods of increasing passive venting to an underslab void

Ventilation efficiency can be increased by several techniques to improve dilution and dispersion of gas to achieve safe acceptable concentrations. These methods are as follows:

- increase the frequency or sectional area of vents to permit a higher rate of air flow into the void and promote cross-wall ventilation

- raise the height of vents on external walls to increase the effect of wind pressures on the system: this can be done using cranked ventilators or vent stacks raised above roof level

- decrease the rate of gas ingress into the void, i.e. reduce the emission rate through the underlying ground by the provision of a low-permeability in-ground barrier: materials which have been used include natural clay, synthetic barriers and mass concrete, and their use as barriers is discussed in Sections 5.4, 5.5 and 8.1.1.

The principles of increasing venting efficiency are illustrated in Figure 30.

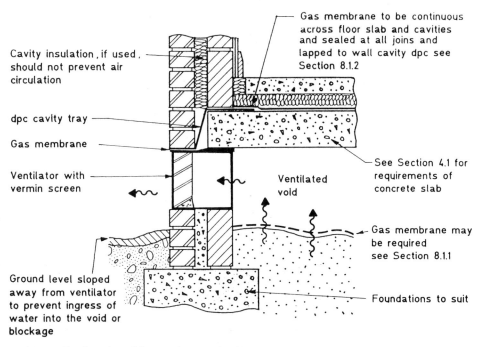

(a) Detail at junction of floor and external wall

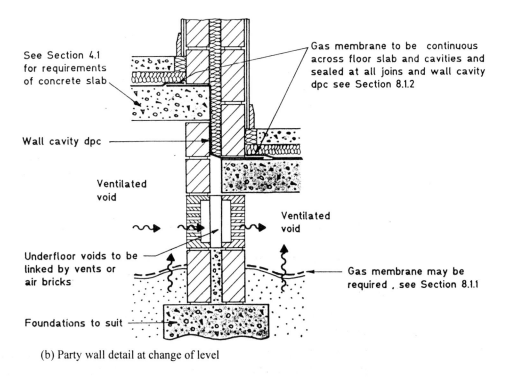

(b) Party wall detail at change of level

Figure 31 Venting arrangements for underslab void

7.1.2   Methods of installation

Construction of an underfloor open void will constrain the structural design of the ground slab and possibly the building. Pre-cast suspended slab construction can to be used to provide an open void beneath the ground floor. This is a relatively common form of construction particularly for small span, lightly loaded developments, e.g. individual residential dwellings. Section 4.1 describes the techniques of ground slab design and construction for gas protection. Figure 31 illustrates various arrangements for providing an underslab void beneath a suspended slab construction. Where underfloor voids are lower than surrounding ground level a straight-sided ventilator cannot be used. In these situations periscope type ventilators are common to overcome installation difficulties (see Figure 39). In all situations a gas membrane will also be required for the reasons described in Section 8.

All external ventilators should be designed to have maximum cross-sectional area for air flow and smooth internal surfaces to minimise resistance and frictional losses. They should be protected by a grille to prevent access to vermin and insects. Where external ventilators may be obstructed by steps or ramps, venting can be achieved by ducting/sleeving ventilators to air vents on the outer construction. Figure 32 illustrates an example of a venting arrangement for residential housing.

An alternative method of providing underfloor ventilation is the use of a granular filled void beneath the ground slab. This form of construction will allow a suspended slab to be cast *in situ* using the granular layer as formwork. The concept of the granular layer is the same as for drainage layers used for in-ground venting of gas discussed in Section 6.1.2. The layer is connected to the exterior of the building by ventilators constructed through the walls. A venting arrangement is illustrated in Figure 33. The advantages and disadvantages of a granular filled void as opposed to an open void are summarised in Table 19.

In order to improve venting efficiency of the granular fill, pipework similar to that used for active abstraction can be installed (see Section 6.2). No specific guidance is available in the UK to allow design of pipework for ventilation purposes beneath buildings, although work is being undertaken at the Building Research Establishment. The Building Regulations Approved Document Part C4 (DoE, 1992) indicates that any pipes that need to carry ventilating air should have a diameter of at least 100 mm.

General aspects which should be considered are:

* spacing of pipework
* length of pipework
* degree of perforation both for gas collection and pipe strength
* strength of pipework which sufficient
* access to the pipework to enable maintenance, rodding and cleaning, etc., to be undertaken.

Air resistance within the pipework should be minimised, so the diameter should be as large as practicable, typically 100 to 150 mm. Internal surfaces of pipes must be smooth, slots or perforations should be preformed circular holes of sufficient size and frequency to allow least resistance to flow of gas. Also acute angle bends in pipework should be avoided.

Figure 32 External ventilation installed in walls and beneath steps

Table 19 Advantages and disadvantages of a granular filled void

Advantages	Disadvantages
• Granular material will encourage mixing of gases which migrate into the void, therefore reducing the hazard of gas layering (see Section 2.3).	• The passive venting efficiency will be reduced because of greater resistance to air flow through the granular material: the consequent reduction in pressure gradient can negate any advantage in reduced void space.
• Reduced volume of the underfloor void due to granular infill will require lower volume flow rate of fresh air to provide adequate ventilation.	• In connection with the above, diffusion is likely to be a predominant process causing dilution and dispersion.
• Cast-in-place suspended floor construction is less likely to have cracks or open joints which might allow gas to ingress into the building fabric (see Section 2.3).	• With time the granular fill may become clogged or blocked with soil fines, dust, weeds, etc., thus reducing its venting efficiency.
• Construction costs can be less expensive than using other forms of ground slab construction.	

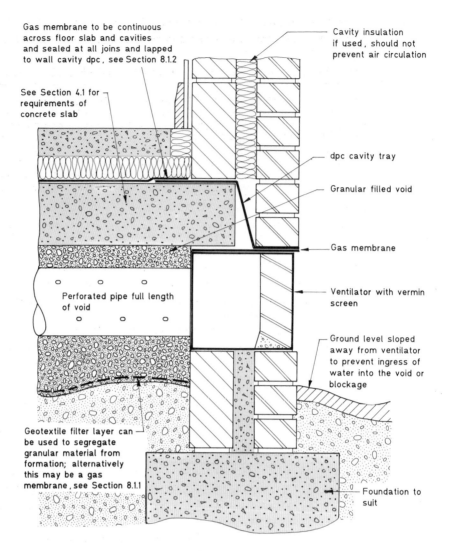

Gas membrane to be continuous across floor slab and cavities and sealed at all joins and lapped to wall cavity dpc, see Section 8.1.2

Cavity insulation if used, should not prevent air circulation

See Section 4.1 for requirements of concrete slab

dpc cavity tray

Granular filled void

Gas membrane

Perforated pipe full length of void

Ventilator with vermin screen

Ground level sloped away from ventilator to prevent ingress of water into the void or blockage

Geotextile filter layer can be used to segregate granular material from formation; alternatively this may be a gas membrane, see Section 8.1.1

Foundation to suit

Figure 33 Venting arrangements for granular filled void

The advantages of pipework incorporated into the granular fill are:

- it allows underfloor passive venting, even if the granular layer becomes impaired due to clogging
- pipework can be maintained and cleaned
- it will allow an active venting system to be installed at a later date, if for any reason passive venting is found to be inadequate because of a change in the gassing regime (see Section 7.2).

The layout of the pipework will, however, be constrained by the building configuration, the inclusion of interior cross walls, downstanding beams or foundations, etc., as well as by the need to provide inlet and outlet ventilation points on all sides to allow for changes in wind direction. Examples of layouts that have been used are shown in Figure 34. Concern has been expressed at the effectiveness of venting pipework to extract gas from the surrounding granular fill. Sheriff *et al.*(1991) indicate that if 20 to 25 mm sized stone is used in a granular filled void which is ventilated by 150 mm diameter pipes at 2 m centres, the resistance from the granular fill is typically 50 to 100 times that of the pipework. Some practitioners have identified problems with systems in which air is drawn through the pipework layout, from one end to the other preferentially, rather than taking gas from the granular fill. This has resulted in a limited zone of extraction around the pipe leaving the bulk of the granular fill 'unvented'. The design spacing of pipes should take account of any likely reduction in the zone of extraction to prevent gas accumulating in localised pockets. Research into the efficiency of pipework to extract gas is currently being undertaken by the NHBC and the BRE.

Box 13 Passive venting to residential development adjacent to landfill

Landfill gas was detected in the course of a ground investigation at a housing development site in Torbay. Methane concentrations ranged between negligible and 5% volume in air. The site itself included an area of made ground comprising mainly inert materials in which gas generation was extremely unlikely. It was suspected that the gas was migrating into the site from adjacent filled ground where former domestic refuse waste disposal was recorded. The presence of landfill gas to the development proposals was highly significant. Unless effective remedial measures could be implemented two extreme possibilities could have jeopardised the development: either abandonment of the site or wholesale removal of the made ground. Furthermore, there was a serious risk of blight to adjoining areas of existing housing.

A gas-control system was implemented as follows:

- maintaining made ground areas as open space: this was achieved by modifying the building plot layout installing a series of passive venting trenches within and around the made ground to prevent further gas migration into the development

- providing suspended ground slabs with open void passive ventilation

- inclusion of gas-resistant membranes and seals to service entry points

- granular gas-drainage layer connected to periphery venting trenches with a low-permeability clay subsoil beneath garden topsoil

- garden sheds, greenhouses, ornamental ponds, etc., were prohibited

- long-term management of the gas-control system including periodic gas monitoring from boreholes and within external vents to the passive venting system beneath properties.

Installation of these protection measures significantly reduced methane concentrations in the ground to less than 0.1% by volume in air. Methane has not been detected within the underfloor void during a period of post-construction monitoring.

The experimental work undertaken in conjunction with the redevelopment of London Docklands, described earlier, demonstrated that dilution and dispersion of methane was much slower from a granular-filled void than an open void and also that gas was more likely to accumulate in confined spaces between the ground slab and the foundations (Carpenter, 1988). Because of this it was recommended that granular-filled voids could only be used where surface emission rates of gas were low and certainly less than 0.01 m/s when measured from a 50-mm diameter borehole. In the majority of case studies reviewed, granular filled voids have been used in situations where the gas concentration is low and there is no detectable gas emission. In other cases it has been used where carbon dioxide was the only gas present and posed no immediate risk to the building or occupants. In these circumstances the use of a granular filled void proved adequate to allow dilution and dispersion of gas by diffusion.

7.1.3 Applications

Passive venting has been applied to many forms of new development ranging from residential dwellings to commercial/retail shops, offices and industrial warehousing. This is partly because the techniques for providing an underslab void, whether open or infilled with granular material, are part of normal building requirements on derelict or filled ground. Given that most sites affected by gas are on filled ground, the need for and cost of providing gas protection measures in the form of an underfloor void are not unduly onerous.

Because passive ventilation does not involve any mechanical or electrical components, it is best suited to those types of development where little or no maintenance or inspection is required for the continuing operation of the system, e.g. private residential development. Once installed, however, a passive venting system cannot easily be changed if greater capacity is needed because of later building modifications (see

Section 11.3). This limitation may render it unsuitable where changes in usage of a building or its function are a requirement of the overall design, e.g. retail shops and warehouses. Examples of the application of passive venting are given in Boxes 13 to 15.

Box 14 Passive venting using granular filled void

Clark *et al.*(1991) describe a leisure development in the West Midlands consisting of a swimming pool and cinema complex. Monitoring of the site for gas indicated concentrations of methane up to 44% LEL and carbon dioxide up to 25% by volume in air although in the area of the proposed building low concentrations and near zero emission rates were recorded. The gas was believed to originate from either organic fill materials buried on the site or underlying Coal Measures strata. The primary protective measure adopted was a granular filled void beneath the ground slab of the building incorporating a system of interconnected pipes with means for active extraction if required. Other protection measures included a low-permeability membrane incorporated into the slab construction with sealed service entries. These types of measures are described in Sections 8 and 12.2, respectively. Gas monitoring was also included in the building design.

Box 15 Passive venting applied to residential development

Carpenter (1988) describes the design of two housing estates in Southern England where detailed assessment of both gas concentrations and surface emission rates was used to establish the design of the underslab passive ventilation system. At one site situated on backfilled gravel workings, methane and carbon dioxide concentrations detected during the investigation were of the order of 20% and 10% by volume in air, respectively, with gas emission rates measured from eight 50-mm diameter boreholes never greater than 0.01 m/s. A passive venting system comprising an open underfloor void (height of void 225 mm with 50% side area of the void ventilated to atmosphere) was used in combination with a low-permeability membrane across the floor slab. At the other site, also an infilled gravel pit, monitoring of boreholes over a five-month period recorded methane concentrations generally over 5% by volume in air with highest concentrations of up to 23% by volume in air. Only one gas emission was recorded over the five-month period of 0.04 m/s in one borehole. No emissions were detected elsewhere. Given the low gassing regime, an open underfloor void was not considered necessary. The ground floor slab was laid on a granular layer and the infilled void ventilated to atmosphere through cranked ventilators situated in the walls of the houses.

7.2 ACTIVE VENTING FOR BUILDINGS

Active venting is the process of ventilating an enclosed space by mechanical pumping in order to induce a pressure gradient relative to atmospheric pressure and create a flow of fresh air. There are three basic types of active ventilation systems applied to buildings and these are:

- mechanical extraction/natural supply
- mechanical supply/natural extraction
- combined mechanical supply/extraction.

Whichever system of active venting is used, the principle controlling methane and associated gases is similar to passive venting as outlined in Section 7.1. An adequate volume flow rate of fresh air, Q, is provided to dilute a gas contaminant entering an enclosed area at surface emission rate, q. The principle is similar to that illustrated in Figure 29 except a mechanical pump produces a pressure gradient which induces a volume flow rate of fresh air. The three types of systems are illustrated in Figure 35 and described below.

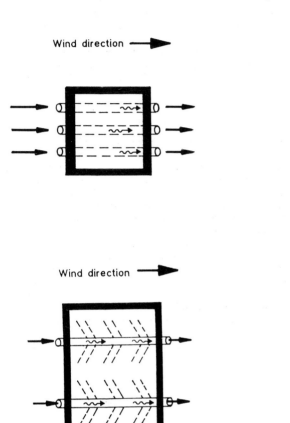

Wind direction ➡

(a) Parallel arrangement: will function with wind direction reversed, but only on two sides of building

Wind direction ➡

(b) Herringbone arrangement: will not function efficiently when wind direction reversed, because gas cannot be drawn easily through acute angled pipework

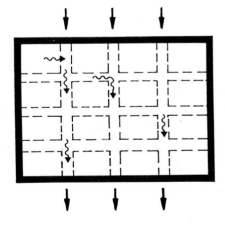

(c) Square grid arrangement: will function regardless of wind direction, but overall efficiency may be low because high resistance from length of pipework and bends

Figure 34 Examples of pipework arrangement in underfloor void

Mechanical extraction/natural supply

This is the simplest form of venting system and comprises one or more fans, usually of the propeller (actual flow or mixed-flow) type installed in outside walls or in the roof. Air is extracted from the confined space so to draw in fresh air.

Alternatively, the system may comprise a range of ductwork arranged for general extraction of foul air or for extraction from localised sources of heat, moisture, odours, fumes and dust. Such ductwork may be connected to centrifugal or axial flow fans that discharge through the wall or roof, terminating in louvres or cowls or a combination of both. The ductwork includes suitable extraction points and dampers. It is essential that provision for replacement air be made and consideration given to the location and size of the inlet.

An extraction system is regarded as a necessary measure to meet the need for ventilation in particularly crowded rooms, offices or restricted areas in which local conditions are likely to prove objectionable as, for example, in lavatories, kitchens, plant rooms and sections of workshops or laboratories; or where there is a statutory requirement for ventilation. Mechanical extraction/natural supply venting systems are the most widely used for the purposes of protecting building structures from gassing ground.

Mechanical supply/natural extraction

This system is similar in form to the extraction system but arranged to deliver fresh air into the enclosed space. Such a system necessitates provision for the discharge of foul air by natural means. Where there is a requirement for the enclosed space to be at a slightly higher pressure than its surroundings (to exclude dust or smoke, for example), the discharge may be through natural leakage paths or balanced pressure relief valves, as may be required. A ducted supply system within a building will normally include an air-cleaning device and an air heater battery with automatic air temperature control. Ducted supply systems can provide better control of air movement.

Combined mechanical supply/extraction

This system is a combination of those described above and comprises supply and exhaust ductwork systems or may employ a common fan with a fresh air inlet on the low-pressure side. In the latter case, an interconnection may be provided to allow partial or full recirculation as required. The fresh air input side of such systems into a building will normally be provided with an air filter and an automatically controlled air heater battery. The ductwork will include suitable dampers, grilles and diffusers. As with ducted supply systems, combined supply and extract systems can provide better control of air movement. These systems are generally not suitable for gas protection since they could potentially involve re-circulation of hazardous gases.

7.2.1   Principles of design

As for passive venting, active venting can be applied in two ways to development affected by methane and associated gases:

1. Dilution and dispersion of gas within the building.

2. Dilution and dispersion of gas before entering the building.

Active venting is normally the only means of providing adequate supply of fresh air in offices, commercial premises, warehouses and light industrial factories, etc., to prevent accumulation of dust, odours, vapours, and gases as well as providing humidity and temperature control. In these circumstances actively ventilated buildings will have, by default, an inbuilt degree of protection against gas ingress. The design of the system should ensure, however, that gas cannot be drawn into the ventilation system at the inlet vent arrangement.

The second means of applying active venting is to dilute and disperse gases before entering the building or structure. This is the most logical practice in that it is better to prevent gas ingress to a building and thus eliminate any risk (see Section 3.3).

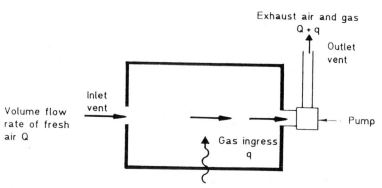

(a) Mechanical extraction/ natural supply

(a) mechanical extraction/ natural supply

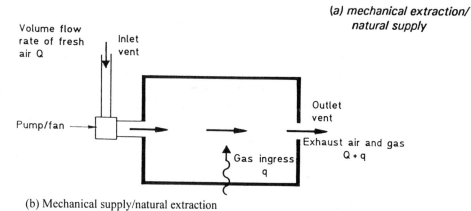

(b) Mechanical supply/natural extraction

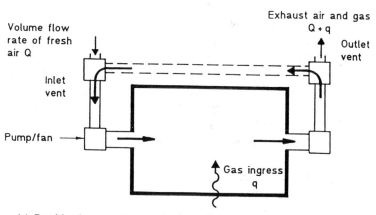

(c) Combined mechanical supply/ extraction

Figure 35 Principal types of active venting systems

The design aspects, methods of installation and constraints on layout are similar to those for passive venting discussed in Section 7.1.2. There are four basic elements to active venting, regardless of the type of system installed, which should be considered. These are as follows.

Underslab venting arrangement

The principle of active venting is to encourage gases accumulating beneath the slab to vent as an exhaust gas to atmosphere. This is achieved by lowering the air pressure beneath the slab to slightly lower than atmospheric pressure. The magnitude of the pressure gradient necessary to ventilate the underslab area adequately will be dictated by the gas regime. In a mechanical extraction/natural supply system gas is diluted by air drawn into the underslab void from an external vent. Suction can also be controlled by providing an additional fan on the inlet vent which is capable of automatic control whilst maintaining the slight suction beneath the slab.

The required volume flow rate of fresh air, Q, to provide adequate dilution of a gas contaminant entering the underslab void of volume, V, at a surface emission rate q, can be found using the formulae set out in Section 7.1.1 and Figure 29. Formulae for designing active venting to provide adequate volume flow rate of fresh air, Q, and air vent requirements can be found in BS 5720:1979. Fans are usually sized to provide a minimum air flow rate sufficient to achieve ventilation rates of between 0.5 and 2 air changes per hour within the underfloor void.

However, as for the design of passive venting, it is necessary that adequate and reliable information is gathered on the gassing regime, particularly about the composition and concentration of individual gases present and the surface emission rate into the underslab void. Gas parameters for the design of the venting system should also reflect future changes in the gas regime. The reasons for this are discussed in Section 2.5.5.

The venting arrangement beneath the ground slab can be either:

- an open underfloor void
- a granular filled void with a network of collector pipes.

The choice between the above methods of extraction depends on the type of development configuration or structural layout of the ground slab as discussed in Section 7.1.2 for passive venting systems. Examples of the application of both arrangements are given in Boxes 16 and 17.

For either arrangement it is usual for the outlet vents of the underslab void to be connected to the extraction pump or fan *via* a manifold duct which runs the length of one side of the building. The manifold duct helps to ensure equal suction pressure is applied to each outlet vent. The general arrangement of an active venting system based on the mechanical extract/natural supply configuration is show in Figure 36.

Monitoring and control system

In order to control the active venting system efficiently an electronic monitoring and control system should be installed. This should measure gas concentrations in the air on the suction side of the extraction pump or fan and at suitable points within the building. These should be in the least well-ventilated rooms, for example in storerooms, WCs, etc. The monitoring and control system should incorporate the following general requirements:

- gas concentrations above a given trigger level in the active venting system should cause the pump or fan to be switched on and the system to operate until the concentration falls below a safe acceptable level
- gas concentrations above a given trigger level in the inside of the building should also switch on the active venting system and trigger an alarm

- the monitoring system should also indicate if the active venting system has failed to operate and that action is required. Monitoring and alarm systems are discussed in Section 9.

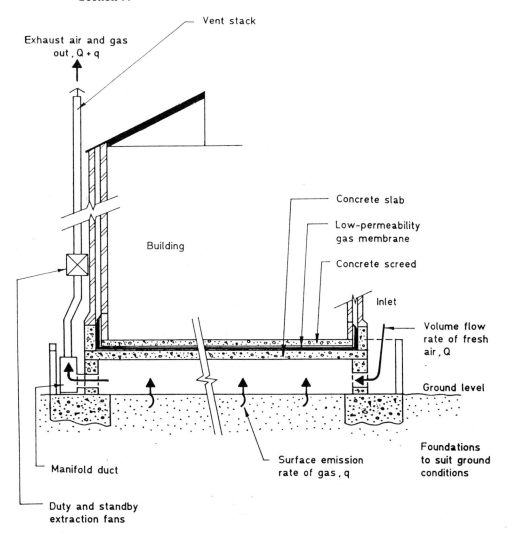

Figure 36 General arrangement of active venting system to underslab void

By their very nature, active venting measures will comprise mechanical and electrical components. All components should be designed to be intrinsically safe. Important aspects are:

- all electrical components should be designed to operate in flammable or explosive atmospheres: reference should be made to the guidance given in BS 5501:1977
- alternatively, all electrical components should be separated and located outside hazardous areas where practical: bifurcated fans driven by a belt attached to an electric motor located in a separate housing have been used in some active venting systems
- the venting system should be able to operate and provide a nominal supply of fresh air by passive venting during periods of non-active operation

- re-circulation of exhaust gases should be prevented and can be achieved by locating the inlet and outlet vents on opposite sides of the building: the requirement for vent stacks is similar to that for passive venting systems discussed in Sections 6.1.2 and 7.1.1.

Box 16 Active venting to underslab void

At a former brickworks site near Wakefield, a large commercial/retail development has been constructed on tipped waste and refuse. Landfill gas was detected with concentrations of methane and carbon dioxide generally less than 1% by volume in air. A comprehensive series of gas protection measures was installed including:

- active ventilation beneath the ground slab of the building
- low-permeability membrane incorporated within the ground slab
- gas detection equipment within the building.

The active venting was installed within an underfloor void beneath the main structural floor. Because of the structural layout of the building the void was divided by ground beams into a series of parallel bays which run the full width of the building, in an east-west direction. The eastern end of each bay was provided with an air inlet protected by grilles. The western end of each bay was connected by ducts through the western edge ground beam to a manifold duct which runs north-south below ground level. Two vertical vent stacks with in-line extraction fans (one duty and one standby in each vertical vent stack) rise from the manifold and vent above roof level. The principle of the design is that any gas emitted from the ground will be mixed with air and drawn through the void to the manifold duct where it is removed up the vent stack by the extraction fans and discharged above roof level of the building. The ventilation rate was calculated to ensure methane concentrations in the underslab void did not exceed 0.5% by volume in air. The fans were designed in accordance with BS 5345: 1976 for electrical apparatus in potentially explosive atmospheres. A standby generator was also installed to provide an alternative source of power in the event of mains power failure.

Gas sensors were located at the exits of the underfloor voids where the manifold duct was positioned to monitor the flow of air coming from each bay of the underfloor void. The sensors were linked to the extraction fans so that if the concentration of methane gas in air at any time exceeds a trigger level of 20% LEL then the fans will be switched to boost extraction to double the normal operational rate.

Commissioning of system

On commissioning it is usual that an active venting system will require on-site adjustments for effective operation. Balancing the fresh air supply is normally required to produce equal suction pressures in the underslab gas collection network. If this is not carried out, then the volume of void nearest the pump will contribute the greatest volume of gas, to the detriment of venting of those compartments furthest from the pump. The frequency of fan operation, and the suction produced, should be matched to the rate at which the gas needs to be extracted. This is achieved as described above regarding the calculation of the volume flow rate of fresh air required in the underslab void.

The monitoring system will require commissioning and testing to ensure that it is operating as required, followed by periodic testing and service, as necessary, at the intervals recommended by the manufacturers.

System operation and maintenance

In keeping with all gas protection measures the active venting will require an operation manual to describe how the system is maintained and should be serviced over the period for which the gas regime continues to present a risk to the development.

The operation manual should also detail the steps to be taken in the event of the failure of the venting system. Adequacy and long-term management needs of gas protection measures are discussed in Section 13.

Box 17 Active venting to granular filled void

Dutton *et al.*(1991) describe the construction of a cinema near Walsall on a former landfill site. The ground investigation indicated up to 7.5 m of made ground comprising mainly putrescible and commercial wastes, overlying glacial drift deposits and Coal Measures strata. Numerous old mineshafts were located on the site with extensive coal and ironstone underground workings. Methane concentrations of up to 40% by volume in air were recorded during the ground investigation. Protection measures to prevent gas ingress into the building fabric included an active venting system below the cinema building floor slab comprising a series of perforated pipes in a gravel surround interconnected to vertical vent stacks.

A mechanical extraction/natural supply venting system was used with extraction fans mounted at roof level. Methane gas sensors were provided at the entry pipe to each fan linked to two control panels. The fans are designed to run at low speed continuously. In the event of gas being detected the fans will switch to high speed for a minimum of 15 minutes.

An extraction system was also installed within the building connected to the air conditioning system. Some 20 gas detectors were installed in the building at strategic locations. In normal air conditioning operations about 50% of the air is recirculated and the remaining 50% being fresh air drawn into the system. If methane is detected at 10% LEL concentrations the system will automatically switch to full extraction with 100% fresh air being introduced.

Other gas protective measures were also incorporated into the development and included a low-permeability gas membrane within the ground slab and passive in-ground venting measures in car park areas. A management manual was prepared detailing maintenance requirements along with contingency plans.

7.2.2 Applications

Active venting is usually applied where the gas regime is sufficiently high in terms of gas concentration or emission rate that reliable continuous control is required to dilute and disperse gas to achieve safe acceptable concentrations. This is particularly the case for methane which could pose an immediate explosive risk if allowed to accumulate. A discussion regarding safe acceptable concentrations of the range of gases associated with methane is given in Section 2.5.5.

Active venting can be used also in a controlled intermittent mode to enhance/boost an existing passive venting system during periods of gas emission when an adequate volume flow rate of fresh air cannot be provided by reliance on natural supply.

However, it should be borne in mind that the operation and requirements on air movement of the two systems can conflict as shown in Figure 37(a) and (b). When combining an active and passive system it is good practice that some form of independent venting arrangement is used, as shown in Figure 37(c) and (d).

In certain situations there may be technical difficulties in combining both venting systems into a building. In these circumstances a solution is to design the venting measures totally as an active system with dual rating; a low rating to provide continuous nominal volume flow rate of fresh air which can be triggered to a higher rating during intermittent periods when hazardous gas concentrations are detected.

With all mechanical installations there will be times when, for maintenance or by failure, an active venting system will not be operational. During these periods gas concentrations may increase to hazardous levels. For this reason active venting on its own cannot be relied upon as a sole means of gas protection. An active venting system should be designed in such a way that it will also operate in a passive venting mode and provide a supply of fresh air for nominal dilution and dispersion.

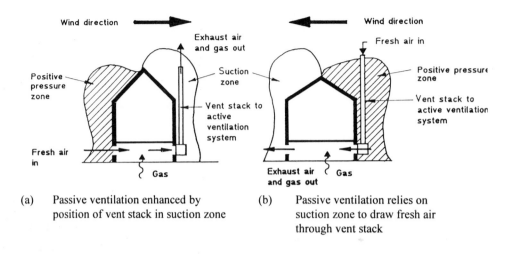

(a) Passive ventilation enhanced by
     position of vent stack in suction zone

(b) Passive ventilation relies on
     suction zone to draw fresh air
     through vent stack

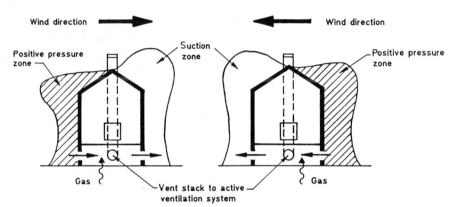

(c) and (d) Vent stack positioned on the exterior gable end of building outside pressure and
suction zones regardless of wind direction; passive ventilation through wall ventilators;
performance independent of vent stack position or wind direction

Figure 37 Venting requirements in combined passive and active systems

Because of the need for installation of mechanical plant, maintenance and control,
active venting systems are best suited to non-domestic dwellings, i.e. commercial or
office development, public buildings, warehouses, etc. For these types of development,
installation, inspection and regular maintenance of the system can be achieved easily
without disruption to occupants or users (see Section 3.1). Figure 38 shows an example
of a vent stack, part of an active venting system to a retail development, which has been
incorporated into the architectural design of the building. In addition, where a
requirement of the development is that the layout and function of buildings can be
altered to suit change in usage, e.g. shopping complexes, supermarkets and warehouses,
the capacity of an active venting system can more easily be changed rather than passive
venting measures. Active venting should be considered essential where there is a risk
that methane in high concentrations and emission rates could accumulate or not be
adequately diluted and would pose an immediate threat of explosion to the
development, occupants and general public in the surrounding environment. Most active
venting systems based on mechanical extraction/natural supply have been designed and
commissioned for this purpose. Systems have been designed to provide enhanced
ventilation within the underfloor void from 1 to 2 air changes per hour up to 8 to 16 air
changes per hour.

Figure 38 Vent stack to actively vented retail development

Sensors installed within the underfloor void trigger the active ventilation system into operation. These trigger concentrations are specific to the type of development, the nature of the migrating gas, the design and capacity of the venting measures and other protection measures installed. Box 16 describes a case study of a dual rated system.

8 Membranes

Membranes are installed within a building or structure to provide a low-permeability barrier against the ingress of gas from the ground into the building fabric. The membrane usually comprises a synthetic sheet or strip of material placed within or beneath the ground slab or walls to form an integral barrier. The low permeability of the membrane resists the flow of gas which is encouraged to migrate to atmosphere on the outside of the structure. Usually passive or active venting is used to dilute and disperse gases beneath the ground slab (see Sections 7.1 and 7.2). Nevertheless, in situations of low gas regime with little or no detectable gas emission a membrane beneath a well, constructed ground slab as described in Section 4.1 may be adequate.

Other terms used for membranes are:

- gas migration barriers
- gas-resistant membranes
- gas-proof membranes
- gas impermeable membranes.

The latter term should not be used as no membrane or barrier is absolutely impermeable.

8.1 PRINCIPLES OF DESIGN AND INSTALLATION

The principles of design and the requirements of a membrane are similar to those of an in-ground barrier discussed in Section 5.2. Essentially the membrane is installed to prevent the ingress of gas through the building fabric *via* such features as:

- porous construction materials
- construction joints and openings
- shrinkage cracks
- service entry points.

The area of greatest concern is the interface between the foundation and ground slab where there are numerous potential entry routes for gas. These entry routes are described in Section 2.3. While the materials of membranes may have permeability values sufficiently low that they can prevent the uncontrolled migration of large volumes of gas, it does not necessarily follow that they will always provide satisfactory performance when laid and installed. Any deterioration in integrity can negate the fundamental objective of the membrane if gas is able to pass through and enter a critical location or region of the building. The parameters which will determine the permeability and performance of the laid and installed membrane are:

- long-term durability: the membrane must perform satisfactorily for as long as a potential risk to the development exists from gas
- resistance to damage during placement and installation from:
  - abrasion
  - puncturing
  - thermal effects including heating/fires causing physical breakdown of the material

- shrinkage
- gaseous vapours, including VOCs causing chemical breakdown of the material
- water and organic solvents
- ultraviolet light causing potential embrittlement of some synthetic materials
- bacteriological action.

The requirements of long-term durability and resistance to mechanical and environmental damage are common to all forms of membranes, regardless of their nature and composition. Table 20 summarises the most widely used membrane materials together with typical values of transmissibility to methane (where published values are available). It should be noted that the value of transmissibility depends on the thickness of the material tested. The typical values quoted in Table 20 are for comparative purposes only between the various materials.

Table 20 Summary of typical materials used for membranes in the UK

Type	Material	Thickness mm	Typical transmissibility to methane ($m^3/m^2/s$ at 1 atm)	
Membrane at formation level	HDPE	1.5 – 3	5×10^{-10}	(1)
	LDPE	0.3 – 1	25×10^{-10}	(1)
	Clay	1000-3000	see note 2	
	Bitumen emulsion	3 – 5	see note 2	
	Mass concrete	100-300	see note 2	
In-structure membrane	LDPE	0.3 – 0.75	$12 – 3.3 \times 10^{-9}$	(3)
	LDPE (carrier) + aluminium foil	0.3 – 0.7	$2500 – 5.5 \times 10^{-12}$	(3)
	LDPE (carrier) + aluminium foil and bitumen	1.5	1.4×10^{-12}	(3)
	HDPE (carrier) + aluminium foil + bitumen polymer	1.5	3.5×10^{-13}	(4)
	Hessian (carrier) + aluminium foil + oxidised bitumen	3.5	7.2×10^{-13}	(4)
	Polyester (carrier) + aluminium foil + bitumen polymer	1.5	7.0×10^{-13} (4)	

Notes:

1. See also Table 16.

2. No published values; dependent on degree of saturation, pore size distribution and spacing. Values of permeability to water for comparative purposes: clay $<1 \times 10^{-9}$ m/s; bitumen emulsion $<1 \times 10^{-9}$ m/s; mass concrete 1 to 20×10^{-13} m/s.

3. Values from Sheriff *et al.*(1991).

4. Values courtesy of Colas Building Products Limited.

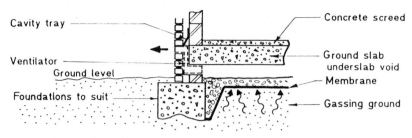

(a) Membrane at formation

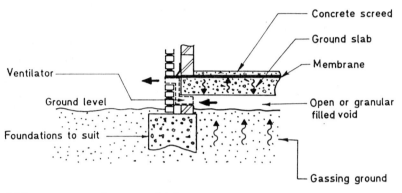

(b) In-structure membrane top of slab

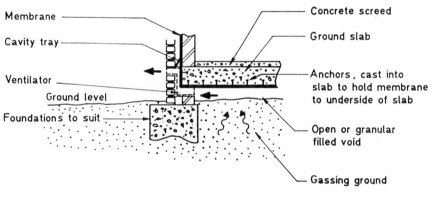

(c) In-structure membrane bottom of slab

Figure 39 Principal types of membrane

There are two principal types of membrane design which have been applied to the protection of buildings/structures:

- membranes at formation level
- in-structure membranes.

Figure 39 shows the principal difference in the application of these membranes.

8.1.1 Membranes at formation level

The purpose of a membrane at formation level is to act in a similar way to a horizontal in-ground synthetic liner as discussed in Section 5.2. The principle of the design is that gas emission from the ground is intercepted before coming into contact with the building fabric. In conjunction with some form of passive or active venting system the gas is encouraged to migrate laterally from beneath the structure and vent at specific locations in a controlled safe environment.

Natural clay when remoulded and compacted can be used to form a membrane at formation level. The clay is compacted within the 'footprint' of the building to provide a barrier against gas migrating upwards to the underside of the ground slab. Other materials that have been used for this purpose are mass concrete or bitumen sprayed on to the ground and allowed to solidify. HDPE and LDPE synthetic membranes used for in-ground barriers have also been used (see Section 5).

The use of a membrane at formation level is appropriate in situations where it would be difficult to attach a membrane direct to or within the ground slab. Examples are timber floors or complex concrete ground slab construction divided by downstanding beams, etc. The use of timber in construction is more common in North America and the Nordic countries where an undercroft (or crawl space) is constructed to locate services beneath the building. In these countries the usual practice is to place a synthetic membrane at ground formation level and protect it with an oversite of mass concrete, as shown in Figure 39(a). It is particularly appropriate for use beneath outbuildings, such as sheds, garages or storerooms or temporary structures where installation of other forms of gas protection cannot be justified on an economic basis.

Table 21 summarises the main advantages and limitations of the use of membranes at formation level.

Table 21 Advantages and disadvantages of membranes at formation level

Advantages	Disadvantages
• Can prevent gas coming into direct contact with the building fabric.	• Remoulded clays need to be placed at a controlled range of moisture content to achieve optimum compaction and low permeability as described in Section 5.4.1.
• Relatively cheap and easy to install.	
• Constructed with few or no joints or welds.	• Natural clays and large mass concrete pours can be subject to shrinkage and cracking because of thermal effects.
• No special methods or fixtures required to allow for the provisions of services, substructures, etc.	• Can rupture with large ground movements in compressible soils, resulting in potentially localised high gas concentrations and emission rates through the membrane.
• Can be made to resist a high degree of wear and tear from construction activities by choice of membrane material, cover protection or thickness.	
• They can accommodate small ground movements and settlement without cracking.	• Difficult to seal membrane adjacent to building foundations because of differential settlement and cracking.
• For certain structures, they may obviate the need for further protective measures, particularly in conjunction with raft foundations see (Section 4.2).	• They can be exposed to aggressive/ corrosive agents within the soil/air environment including biological attack which may limit their durability.

Differential settlement between the building foundations and formation should be allowed for in the choice of the membrane, particularly if the membrane is to be placed on poorly compacted ground or soft highly compressible soils. In these situations a synthetic membrane can be used, but placed with adequate slack and folds to accommodate movement, although this is difficult to achieve in practice except by careful workmanship. In addition, the membrane may also need to be placed over or on steel reinforcement from ground beams or piles to give a gas tight seal at the foundation/membrane interface. Careful workmanship will be needed to cut the membrane to fit over protruding bars and the resulting hole sealed with a flexible sealant as shown in Figure 40(a).

A circular or square concrete or steel pile protruding through the membrane can be sealed by the use of specially pre-fabricated sections of membrane (known as a 'top hat') as shown in Figure 40(b). This comprises a circular sleeve or corner section and a flat strip finished with a covering strip of gas-resistant self-adhesive material. The detail is similar in form to that used for service pipes through the membrane as described in Section 12.2 and shown in Figure 50.

8.1.2   In-structure membranes

In-structure membranes are installed within the building fabric to seal all construction joints, at ground slab/foundation level, gaps and cracks over the plan area of the building. The reason for this is described in Section 4.1. The concept is similar to the installation of conventional barriers to prevent moisture or damp invading the building fabric from the ground. Indeed the basic designs and materials used for damp-proofing have been adapted for gas protection to buildings and structures.

In the USA, other techniques have been tried to seal the building fabric itself against gas ingress. First *et al.*(1986) describe the use of cement-based grouts/screed, asphalt emulsions or sodium silicate gels applied to concrete ground slabs to provide gas protection. However, these materials have had little success on their own in sealing construction joints. Unlike synthetic liners used for in-ground barriers and membranes placed at formation level (see Sections 5.2 and 8.1.1) structural membranes have to be pliable to mould around construction detailing and acute angles. This requirement means that the synthetic liner needs to be relatively flexible and thin, certainly thinner than the liners used to form in-ground barriers. In the UK the most widely used synthetic materials to form structural membranes are:

- LDPE
- LDPE composite materials
- HDPE composite materials.

Generally these materials have low transmissibility to both methane and carbon dioxide. However, because of the relative thinness and flexibility, their durability and long-term performance are often uncertain. For this reason composite materials based on these products have been devised which incorporate a thin sheet of aluminium to provide the low-permeability element. The aluminium foil is sandwiched between thin sheets of the synthetic element for protection. Table 20 gives typical transmissibility values to methane for stated thicknesses of material.

(a) Sealing steel reinforcement from foundation through membrane

(b) Prefabricated membrane sections around piles

Figure 40 Placement of membrane at foundation interface

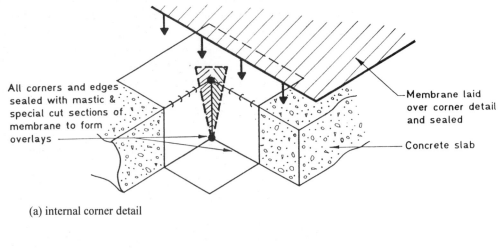

All corners and edges sealed with mastic & special cut sections of membrane to form overlays

Membrane laid over corner detail and sealed

Concrete slab

(a) internal corner detail

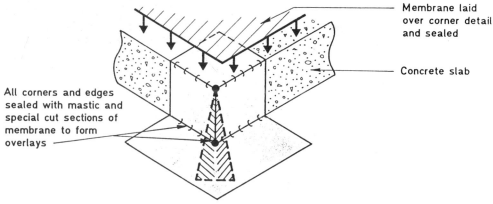

Membrane laid over corner detail and sealed

Concrete slab

All corners and edges sealed with mastic and special cut sections of membrane to form overlays

(b) external corner detail

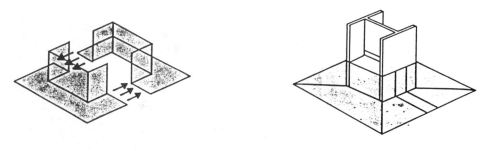

(c) column detail

Figure 41 Typical preformed membrane sections

Other synthetic materials have been used such as thin-gauge polyethylene sheeting and polyvinyl chloride (PVC). This is common practice particularly where carbon dioxide is perceived to be the predominant problem. However, while they may be impermeable enough to provide gas protection, they have relatively low strength and durability. This is particularly significant during construction when integrity can easily be destroyed by construction activities.

Manufacturers of synthetic membranes provide instructions on how to lay and install them correctly. The main matters to be considered with respect to the installation of these membranes are discussed by BRE (1991c). Protection for both sides of the membrane should be provided. The membrane should be protected once laid either by the use of temporary boarding or sheeting over the whole area. This is not always practical during construction operations because of the need to make provisions for service connections into the building, and for the construction of internal walls, substructures, etc. Service entries into buildings are discussed in Section 12.2. Protection of composite membranes is especially important, particularly those incorporating aluminium foil. This is because if the aluminium is exposed during installation it can be chemically attacked and dissolved by alkalis present in wet concrete or mortar, with the possible evolution of hydrogen gas.

(a) Membrane sealed around stanchion bases and acting as dpc across wall cavity

(b) Membrane laid over large concrete slab prior to placement of concrete screed

Figure 42 Use of in-structure membranes

Separate membranes should be overlapped, rolled or taped to ensure continuity. Alternatively, sheets can be welded or sealed in bituminous emulsion although care should be taken to avoid damaging the membrane by excessive heating or burning (see Section 12.2). Specially prepared sections of membrane should be used to seal edges and corners around floor slabs, ground beams, columns, etc. These can be either preformed in the manufacturing process or assembled on site. Sections preformed at the point of manufacture are likely to be less prone to imperfections and should be used in preference where possible. Some typical details are shown in Figure 41.

All in-structure membranes should be continuous across the entire plan area of the building/structure to the external face on all sides of the building. This includes sealing across cavity walls and voids formed in hollow concrete block walls, etc., to prevent gas accumulating in them. To achieve this it is necessary to modify traditional construction practice and ensure a higher than normal level of workmanship. For example, in a cavity wall the normal and separate dpc in each leaf has to be supplemented with the membrane carried through to the external wall. During construction care is needed to ensure that the membrane is not damaged and that all joints in the membrane are sealed across the cavity, not just lapped.

Precautions should also be taken to minimise possible differential movement/settlement between walls, ground slab and the membrane. Provision for this should be made at wall and slab joints by appropriate detailing at design stage. This will require adequate overlaps of material at joints and sealing with a suitable sealant which will remain flexible at all times even at temperatures below freezing point. Generally the minimum overlap of a welded membrane should be 150 to 200 mm. Particular attention should be given to ensure membrane integrity around columns and walls.

Some membranes may also act as a dpm and/or dpc for water vapour and moisture control. Where this is not the case a separate membrane will need to be incorporated into the construction detail. All membranes should be inspected for satisfactory workmanship on completion of installation, before covering with structural concrete or floor screed finish, etc. Any damage or tears should be repaired. This inspection should be undertaken by the membrane installer who can readily undertake the necessary and appropriate form of repair.

Box 18 Installation of a membrane within a ground slab

A development comprising seven two-storey business units with two linked warehouse units has been constructed on a site which had been used for gravel and clay extraction. The thickness of the backfill was some 7 m and was found to be gassing at levels of up to 5% by volume of methane in air. The protection of the buildings against methane included:

- a low-permeability gas barrier into the ground slab
- passive ventilation of underslab voids
- provision of mechanical ventilation if required together with sensors and monitoring devices.

Placing the membrane above the ground slab beneath a concrete screed was considered inappropriate as heavy floor loadings were expected to cause spalling of a thin floor screed on a polyethylene membrane. It was decided to locate the barrier beneath the ground slab placing it on permanent shuttering that spanned between pile caps and ground beams. The shuttering was constructed from 51-mm wide galvanised steel strips some 0.9-mm thick on which 35-mm polystyrene board was placed to form a flat surface. On this surface two layers each consisting of a composite sheet of LDPE incorporating aluminium foil were laid with staggered laps. The assembly was held together using galvanised fasteners. Where the fasteners penetrated the membrane the hole was sealed with bitumen mastic. The surface of the membrane was protected using permanent self-adhesive protection boards. The reinforcement and concrete for the ground slab were then placed on the protection boards. At downstanding beams and at underslab ventilation slots, the membrane was wrapped around to give continuity.

8.2 APPLICATIONS

Membranes are the most widely used single form of gas protection for buildings/ structures. They have been adapted to fit most forms of building layout to provide an integral seal. Parker (1986) and Barry (1987) describe the general use of membranes to protect development from the effects of methane and carbon dioxide. Carpenter (1988) describes the use of membranes in conjunction with passive venting to protect housing development from landfill gas. Some typical details of structural membrane applications are shown in Figure 42. Membranes can be used to protect structures not only from methane and associated gases, but also from radon (BRE, 1991c) and VOCs (Fugler, 1992).

Box 18 describes a typical application and use of membranes. Other case studies where membranes have been incorporated as part of a number of gas protection measures are described in Boxes 13 and 16.

9 Gas monitoring and alarms

Gas monitoring is important for any development affected by methane and associated gases. It is required not only at the investigation and design stage of a development project but also during construction and subsequently in the long term. Table 22 summarises the need for gas monitoring during each stage of development.

Table 22 Gas monitoring requirements during development

Phase of development	Purposes	Duration
Feasibility	Monitoring unlikely except as preliminary spiking survey if visual or documented evidence is found.	
Site investigation	To establish: • gas composition • gas concentration • gas emission rates • variations with time and meteorological condition.	Over not less than 3 and preferably more than 6 months
Construction	To monitor change in gas regime To ensure safe working conditions.	Throughout construction period
Post-construction and long term	To check that protection measures are working To give early warning of a hazardous situation To check that there is an off-site investigation affecting adjacent development	Continuing or at periodic intervals

Note: The frequency of taking measurements depends on the situation and the information needed, ranging from near-continuous observations to readings at intervals of weeks.

The extent of gas monitoring required at each stage of development will depend on the nature of the gas regime, the quality and reliability of the monitoring data obtained and the scope of protection measures adopted. Gas monitoring can also be used to safeguard the occupants of existing development potentially affected by gas (see Section 11.2).

Alarm systems are an extension to gas monitoring. They provide an audible or visual warning when gas concentrations exceed pre-set criteria when specific action is required. The alarm system may be integral with the gas monitoring device or remotely connected by telemetric link or other signalling devices to a control centre.

9.1 GAS MONITORING EQUIPMENT

The variety of instruments available for monitoring gases is large, ranging from relatively simple detector tubes to complex micro-processor controlled multi-point sampling systems. Crowhurst and Manchester (1993) provide useful guidance to available instruments and methods to detect and monitor gases. For all types of instruments the principal components are broadly similar. These are:

- a gas sampling device

- a sensor to detect the gas to be measured

- an analyser to interpret and quantify the concentration of the sampled gas

- a means of outputting the measurement, either as a result or an output signal to a remote control module.

Monitoring can be either periodic, using portable instruments, or continuous using permanently installed equipment. Each type of instrument has its own advantages and limitations which may restrict its use in specific circumstances. Safety in the use of gas instruments and monitoring procedures is very important. Useful guidance on safe monitoring procedures is given in Waste Management Paper No. 27 (DoE, 1991). It should be borne in mind that not all gas monitoring instruments are completely intrinsically safe. To comply with established codes of practice and directives, all gas monitoring instruments should be certified for use by BASEEFA or CENELEC or other recognised authority.

The type of monitoring equipment should be chosen to suit the nature and use of the development and the composition and concentration of gas. Specific guidance on the methods of measuring and monitoring methane and associated gases is given by Crowhurst and Manchester (1993), Waste Management Paper No. 27 (DoE,1991) and Tonkyn (1989). These documents provide detailed information on the instruments available, their applications, advantages and limitations. The most commonly used instruments for on-site measurement of methane and associated gases during construction or long-term monitoring within buildings are detectors operating on one or more of the following types of sensor principles:

- infra-red absorption

- catalytic oxidation

- thermal conductivity.

Table 23 summarises the typical applications of these instruments and additional details are given below. They offer a wide range of sensitivity and although not suited for sampling the ambient atmosphere (where the concentrations of gas may be very low), on gassing sites they have found considerable use in enclosed atmospheres, in sampling from surface cracks and fissures, and from purposely installed sampling points.

Other types of instruments and detection techniques which can be used in the context of building development are:

- flame ionisation detectors

- gas chromatography

- chemical indicator tubes

- semiconductor detectors

- electrochemical cells.

Table 23 Typical applications of available gas monitoring instruments

Gas	Sensor Type	Range	Sensitivity	Application
Methane	Catalytic	0–100%LEL 0–10% LEL	± 2% LEL ±0.5% LEL	Suitable for monitoring low levels (<5% vol) of flammable gas if sufficient oxygen is present.
	Thermal conductivity *	0–100% vol	± 2%	Suitable for monitoring methane and carbon dioxide but must be calibrated for required gas.
	Infra-red	0–100% vol 0–10% vol	± 3% ± 1%	Suitable for monitoring methane and carbon dioxide.
Carbon dioxide	Thermal conductivity	0–100% vol	± 10%	Suitable for use in the presence of methane and air. Should be calibrated for gases required.
	Infra-red	0–100% vol 0–10% vol 0–5% vol	± 0.3% ± 0.3% ± 0.01%	Suitable for monitoring carbon dioxide in the presence of methane and air.

Note: *   Methane detectors operating on thermal conductivity principle are usually equipped with catalytic detectors for LEL ranges.

These techniques are best used, for monitoring short- and long-term exposure of personnel exposed to toxic hazardous gases such as hydrogen sulphide, or where there might be oxygen depletion, or where detection of gases at very low concentrations is required.

Infra-red absorption

Instruments based on infra-red absorption offer probably the most reliable method of on-site measurement in the context of building development for the detection and monitoring of methane and carbon dioxide. The advantages and disadvantages are summarised in Table 24.

Refinements of these instruments are laser detection systems (LIDAR) and differential absorption laser detection systems (DIAL). These systems are essentially an extension of the infra-red type of instrument in which a tuneable laser is used to provide an intense narrow-band source of infra-red radiation at a selectable wavelength. The laser beam is directed through the portion of the atmosphere to be measured until it hits a suitably sited retro-reflector which returns the beam back along its original path for measurement by a detector close to the laser. The amount of target gas in the chosen atmosphere is measured by observing the reduction in laser beam intensity due to absorption by the gas. The main advantage of these instruments is that they can scan across large surfaces of a site or plan area of a building. As well as being able to locate the main methane emission areas of a site, this system can also determine the total flow rate of methane emitted.

Table 24 Advantages and disadvantages of instruments based on infra-red absorption

Advantages	Disadvantages
The detection method does not consume any component of the sample, and allows optional recirculation of the sample even on small volumes of material.	The presence of water in the gas, particularly if it condenses in the sample cell, will affect the readings.
The sampling cell can be made small enough to fit in the *insitu* sampling point so that measurements can be made without physically removing the sample.	A dirty sampling cell can cause the instrument to under-read.
The detection system does not require the presence of oxygen.	
The detection system can be made essentially specific to a particular gas, significantly reducing the effects of cross-interference from other gases in the sample.	
The output from many sensors can be linked to form a network to provide continuous long-term monitoring.	
The sensor cannot be desensitised.	
Sensors operating with different infra-red wavelengths can be incorporated into a single sensing head to allow simultaneous measurement of more than one gas, e.g. methane and carbon dioxide.	

Catalytic instruments

Instruments based on catalytic oxidation are probably the most widely used type of methane gas detector because of their relatively low cost and ease of operation. Although usually calibrated for methane in air for the 0% to 100% LEL range (0% to 5% methane by volume in air) this type of instrument will detect any flammable gases (e.g. hydrogen and VOCs).

Although the response of the instrument will be similar for any flammable mixture in terms of the percentage LEL measured, the absolute concentration will differ for different gases. Therefore, to convert accurately the LEL measurement of a single flammable gas to a concentration in percentage by volume in air, the instrument should preferably only be used and calibrated with the gas it is intended to measure. Alternatively, an instrument may be calibrated with a single flammable gas, e.g. pentane or acetone, and the manufacturer's conversion tables used to correct for different gases. General manufacturing standards and operating guidelines for these types of instruments are given in BS 6020:1981. The advantages and disadvantages of instruments based on catalytic oxidation are summarised in Table 25.

The majority of commercially available instruments based on catalytic oxidation are combined with a thermal conductivity sensor. This allows the addition of an extra measuring range (0% to 100% by volume).

Table 25 Advantages and disadvantages of instruments based on catalytic oxidation

Advantages	Disadvantages
Capable of detecting low concentrations of gas (typically 2% LEL).	The sensor is not gas specific.
Can be made easily into a portable instrument.	The sensor requires oxygen.
Relatively low cost.	The sensor may become saturated.
	In producing an output the sensing element destroys the sample (by oxidation).
	At very high concentrations this type of sensor will read zero. In its crudest form this type of sensor will read less than 100% LEL for concentrations above the UEL, as a result of insufficient oxygen being available to oxidise the flammable gas. This is a potentially dangerous feature which can be overcome by coupling the catalytic sensor with the output from a thermal conductivity sensor.
	Catalyst poisoning may de-activate the sensor.
	Sensor deterioration may occur with age.

Thermal conductivity

Gas detection instruments of this type can measure the total concentration in a gas sample of all flammable gases and carbon dioxide present by comparing the thermal conductivity of the sample against an internal electronic standard representing normal atmospheric air. They can measure the full 0% to 100% range of gas concentrations, although sensitivity at low concentrations, below the LEL of flammable gases, is poor. With binary or mixed gases, e.g. landfill gas, additional problems occur as each gas affects the thermal conductivity cell differently. Manufacturers can calibrate instruments for binary gas mixtures, but this will limit their application and use to specific locations. The main advantages and disadvantages of these instruments are listed in Table 26.

Both catalytic and thermal conductivity detectors can be combined into the same instrument and share a common display. Apart from the individual comments above regarding these types of instruments, the following are points to note when using these combined or coupled devices. Combined catalytic and thermal conductivity instruments, being easily portable devices as well, can be used as the basis for multi-point fixed systems. A common major problem with these instruments is that they only provide a fixed point value, i.e. gas concentrations at the sensor location. Therefore the correct monitoring position is essential, particularly within a building. This problem, to a certain extent, can be overcome using infra-red absorption techniques as described earlier. It should be recognised, that with the two different methods of detection being used in a combined instrument the LEL scale cannot be regarded as a sensitive expansion of the percentage volume in air scale. Both types of detectors require the sample gas to be drawn in a continuous stream. The volume of sample required may exceed the ability of the space being monitored to be recharged with gas, if its volume is small. In these circumstances air may be drawn into the space and non-representative readings obtained.

Table 26 Advantages and limitations of instruments based on thermal conductivity

Advantages	Disadvantages
Can be used to determine the concentration up to 100% by volume of any gas present in the reference gas, normally ambient atmospheric air.	Cannot distinguish between gases or gas mixtures which have the same thermal conductivity.
Can be easily combined with other detectors.	The presence of other gases with different thermal conductivities can influence the readings in some instruments.
	Errors can occur at low gas concentrations.

9.2   APPLICATIONS

As indicated in Table 22, the extent and scope of gas monitoring depends on its particular purpose and phase of development. Gas monitoring using portable instruments is commonly used during the site investigation and construction phases of development. For residential development long-term gas monitoring using portable equipment is often the only means of recording the gas regime below new or existing development and/or installed gas protection measures, because of the difficulty of installing equipment in households or private property where access for maintenance and servicing would be required. This can also lead to the more difficult problem of blight and reduction in market property values. These difficulties are discussed in Section 10 in relation to the wider issue of the problems of long-term management of gas control systems for development. In practice, gas monitoring for new and existing housing development has been undertaken either by:

- boreholes surrounding the development where periodic access can be gained to measure gas concentrations using portable instruments
- discrete monitoring points built into the building allowing readings to be taken using portable instruments, as shown in Figure 43.

Permanently installed equipment tends to be used in developments such as retail shops, warehouses, offices and buildings accessible to the general public. This is because these types of development usually have a planned and managed maintenance programme which encompasses all building services, e.g. ventilation, air conditioning, heating and lighting. Gas monitoring can be easily incorporated into the management programme. Such equipment has also been installed in flatted dwellings or housing where a common building management service or trust exists to provide maintenance to the development. Examples of gas monitoring are given in Boxes 19 to 21. In such situations permanently installed gas monitoring instruments are connected by cables to a central control module. Each instrument is connected to its own circuit-board known as a control card within the control module and incorporates individual display readouts and alarm settings. An automatic data logging system provides the most efficient and convenient method of obtaining and then storing data from gas monitoring instruments. Some data loggers allow extra memory to be added and other parameters to be measured, such as water levels, conductivity, or pH values. Loggers can also be used to trigger alarms when a preset safety level has been exceeded. In addition, they can be used to transmit the monitoring information from the control module by signal off site to a continuously manned station capable of receiving alarm signals and taking appropriate action. The possible combinations of instruments, control module data logger, and signalling link, are many and can be tailored to specific requirements.

Dutton *et al.* (1991) describe the installation of a gas monitoring and alarm system within a cinema complex in Nottingham. The gas monitoring system is used to control the active ventilation system by automatically switching the active ventilation system to full capacity when methane greater than 10% LEL is detected. A fuller description of this case study is given in Box 17.

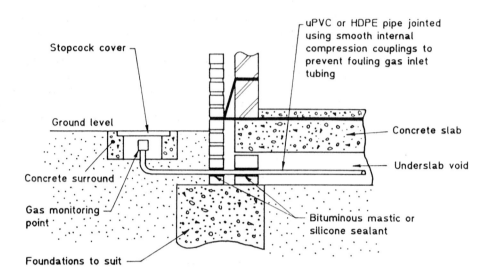

(a) Monitoring point at ground level

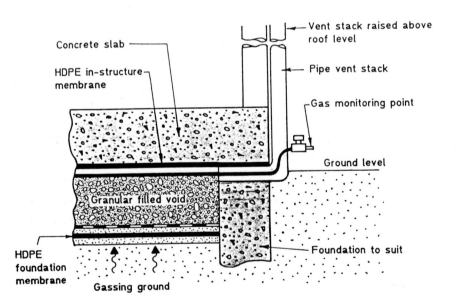

(b) Wall mounted monitoring point

Figure 43 Typical arrangements for gas monitoring points

In-ground gas monitoring

There are three basic types of gas monitoring systems which can be applied. These are:

- central sequential
- local sequential
- in-place sensor.

Box 20 Monitoring of passive venting system

At a multi-storey residential development near Dartford, Kent, constructed adjacent to a landfill site, the gas protection measures comprise in-ground perimeter ventilation trenches and passive ventilation beneath structures. No methane has been detected on the site on the basis of measurements using portable gas detection equipment. However, permanent gas monitoring equipment and alarms have been installed in the ventilation trenches surrounding the development but not in the buildings, as an additional level of security, to warn of any increase in gas migration passing through the ventilation trenches. The gas sensors have been linked to central data loggers within the public lobby of one of the flat units. The data logger and control module are connected by telemetry link to two independent companies who provide continuous monitoring and response to any alarm. The alarm has been set to trigger at 0.5% methane by volume in air (10% LEL).

In the 24 months of operation, the alarm is understood to have been triggered twice. On both occasions this was traced to faults within the gas monitoring system or leaks from natural gas supplies

Typical situations in which these systems can be applied together with their limitations are described below.

Central sequential system

This consists of a gas monitoring instrument and a data logger which are connected to gas sampling points, e.g. boreholes around the site. The instrument draws gas from each borehole sequentially through tubes of about 6 mm in diameter (see Figure 44). There are a number of drawbacks with this system. These are as follows:

- water vapour present in the gas can condense and block the sampling lines
- the condensate itself may give off gas, affecting the readings; to overcome the problems of condensation, filters should be used
- the gas has to be flushed right through the sampling tubes in order to obtain an accurate reading
- sampling time may be long if the sample lines are long
- a large amount of gas will be withdrawn if the sample lines are very long
- withdrawing large volumes of gas disturbs the sampling zone and may cause sample dilution
- if a problem occurs with the monitoring instrument and/or data logger all the readings will be lost.

Local sequential system

This type of system is essentially a localised version of the central sequential system. A small number of instruments can be connected to a control module and data logger, which is in turn connected to others in a loop (see Figure 44b). A master data logger can be connected to the system to gather data from the local loggers around the development. The advantages of this system over a central sequential system are:

- a problem with one sensor will not affect the readings from the others, only those on the loop to which it is connected
- the nearer the data logger is located to the sampling points, the more accurate the readings
- disturbance of the sampling zone is reduced.

With both the local and central sequential systems the loop can be expanded or shortened as necessary to include the required number of sampling points.

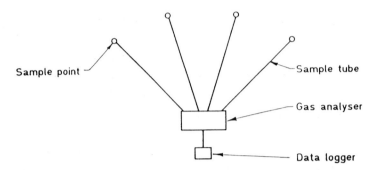

(a) Central sequential

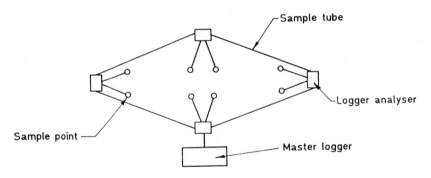

(b) Local sequential

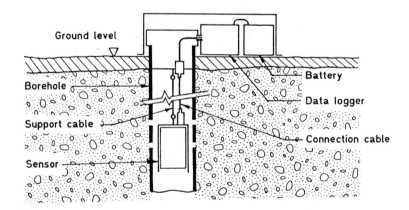

(c) In-place sensor

Figure 44   Layout arrangements for in-ground gas monitoring systems (after Crowhurst and Manchester, 1993)

In-place sensor system

This system is designed to record the data obtained from a single instrument located in a fixed position, e.g. within a borehole. Each instrument is linked to a data logger and control module situated on the surface (see Figure 44c). Each data logger can support up to several instruments and can also be connected to a master data logger if more comprehensive monitoring is required. The advantages of this system are:

- instantaneous gas readings are obtained
- minimal disturbance of sampling zone
- individual sensors can be programmed to take readings automatically at pre-set intervals.

Gas monitoring within buildings

The purpose of monitoring the concentration of gas within a building is to ensure that its atmosphere is safe and that gas protection measures incorporated into the building development to control gas are working efficiently. There are two principal considerations in the design of any system for this purpose:

- choosing the type of instrument most suitable
- the location of the instruments.

Any of the instruments and sensors described in Section 9.1 can be used as the basis for a multi-point fixed sampling system, although the most commonly used are probably the catalytic and infra-red based systems. These can be linked to automatic data logging and warning systems connected either optically or electronically to a single central micro-processor based control module. The various configurations of data logging systems discussed in Section 9.2.1 can be applied to monitoring within buildings. A typical gas monitoring system within a building is shown in Figure 45 where a number of sensors (not shown) are connected to a control and alarm unit.

Whichever gas monitoring system is used there will be an on-going requirement for maintenance, checking, and calibration of the instruments. Many systems which are micro-processor controlled have self-check facilities which will assist this process and give an early warning of detector failure. It may also be advisable in sensitive areas to fit two types of detector at the same location. This can help avoid problems of 'common mode failure' in similar detectors failing from the same fault whether electrical or as a result of sampling conditions.

There are many uncertainties and misconceptions concerning the positioning of monitoring instruments in buildings for the purpose of measuring gases which may enter from the ground. These tend to arise because no account is taken of the influence of other gases (e.g. carbon dioxide) on the nature of the mixture in terms of flammability, buoyancy and toxicity. For example, landfill gas being a mixture principally of methane and carbon dioxide (see Section 2.4) has a buoyancy that varies depending on the exact composition and temperature of the mixture. For a typical mixture, i.e. between 45% and 65% methane, the buoyancy is close to that of air, being either slightly more (65% CH_4) or slightly less (45% CH_4) buoyant than air. In addition, if the landfill gas contains nitrogen or is diluted by air before it enters the building, the buoyancy may be very similar to that of air. Under either circumstance the effect of buoyancy is therefore small and the behaviour of the gas will be governed to a great extent by the natural air flows, temperature and ventilation within the building (see Section 2.4).

In most situations where gas can enter from the ground below a building, gas sensors should be sited as close as possible to the likely routes of ingress at whatever height they exist. Additional sensors at ceiling height may provide further safety, but they should not be relied upon as the only location. Entry routes for gas into buildings/structures are discussed in Section 2.3.

For general guidance, gas sensors within a building should be located in the following areas:

- rooms with little or no natural ventilation
- rooms containing potential sources of ignition, particularly electrical equipment, gas burners or boilers
- underfloor and wall cavities where gas may collect and migrate
- ducts and, if placed within the ground, sewers and drainage channels, which may form routes for gas ingress
- as close as practicable to potential gas ingress points, e.g. wall/floor joints, service inlet points.

Useful guidance on the position of gas monitoring equipment in buildings is given by Crowhurst (1987) and Creedy (1990).

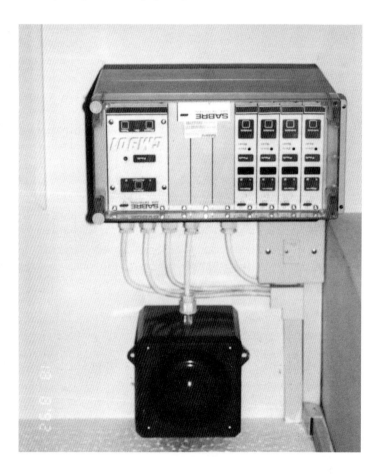

Figure 45 Example of installed gas monitoring system within a building

Box 21 Monitoring of passive venting to existing residential development

Gas monitoring and alarm systems are of particular value as a safety precaution in existing buildings affected by gassing ground. In such circumstances remedial methods of ventilation or in-ground barriers may be only partially effective and a system of gas monitors and alarms can provide a means of measuring their performance. Carden *et al.*(1983) describe the use of gas monitoring of an existing residential suburb on the outskirts of Barnsley affected by surface emission of methane. Passive in-ground ventilation trenches were used to control methane migration to existing development. Continuous monitoring for methane was undertaken by installing monitoring equipment in houses in the worst affected residential area. The sensors were installed within the cavity walls of the houses. A summary of procedures to be adopted if and when methane was detected is shown in the figure below.

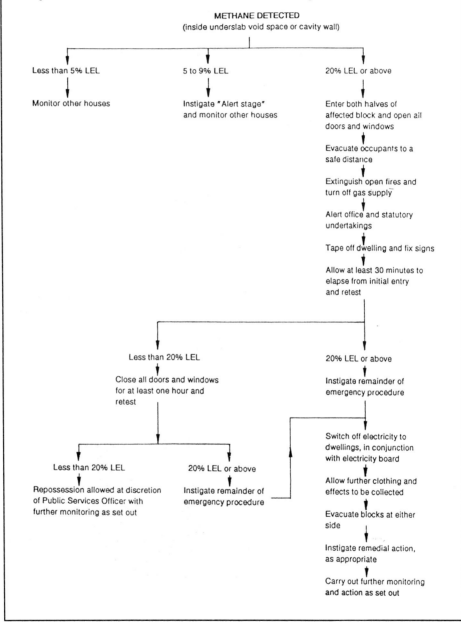

Depending on particular circumstances the gas monitoring equipment will incorporate or be linked to an alarm system which will be triggered when gas concentrations are detected at certain pre-determined levels. For methane, alarm systems typically involve at least two trigger points of activation as follows:

1. A low-level alarm to provide a warning that gas concentrations have exceeded safe acceptable levels for air quality. This could also be linked to switching on an active

venting system (see Section 7.2) or call-out of service personnel to check the operation of the gas protection measures and verify and undertake additional gas monitoring. The gas levels will be appropriate for the perceived risk to the development from the particular gas or gases. Typically this level is set at 5% or 10% LEL depending on specific circumstances.

2. A high-level alarm to indicate gas concentrations in excess of maximum permitted levels and that immediate action is required (this might involve evacuation of the buildings). In the case of methane the higher level of alarm is usually set at 1% to 2.5% by volume in air (20% LEL) at which point the building should be evacuated.

Waste Management Paper No. 27 (DoE, 1991) provides guidance on trigger concentrations for methane and carbon dioxide in buildings and advice on recommended action.

Box 21 describes a case where gas monitoring to existing residential development was undertaken to assess the effectiveness of gas protection measures. Other examples of the use of gas monitoring and alarm equipment to protect existing development and buildings are described in Boxes 27 and 28.

10 Gas-control systems

The gas protection measures, as described in Sections 4 to 8, are wide and diverse. Each measure has its own advantages and disadvantages and is therefore more suitable in certain situations and types of development than in others. Furthermore, no protective measure on its own is immune from factors unknown to or out of the control of the designer. In that such factors might lead to failure, individual protective measures are usually combined to form a gas-control system. In this way the probability of failure or of gas passing each individual protection measure in the system diminishes as the number of measures increases. In other words, the potential fallibility and limitations of individual protective measures can be accepted as the likelihood of simultaneous failure of all measures becomes remote. The number and type of protective measures provided in a gas-control system should be related to the level of risk of failure that can be tolerated for a particular development.

Factors which directly influence the level of risk and therefore the number of measures in a control system are:

- nature and composition of gas or gases
- the gas emission rate
- prediction of the future gas regime and its behaviour
- the type of development
- the ability to provide long-term management of the gas-control system
- the need for and ease of maintenance of the gas-control system
- public acceptance of the principle of gas protection to development
- public acceptance of the level of risk.

Other factors such as capital and running costs of the gas-control system and their energy efficiency when considering active venting systems also influence the number of measures to be provided.

10.1 SYSTEMS USED FOR METHANE AND CARBON DIOXIDE

Information gathered for the preparation of this report indicates a distinct difference in the perceived level of risk to development depending on the nature and composition of gas. Most case studies of development affected primarily by methane have incorporated a minimum of three or more individual protective measures to create an effective control system. This is because of the immediate hazard and perceived risk that occurs if methane is allowed to accumulate to an explosive limit. In broad terms these three measures are usually:

1. Primary measure: in-ground venting of the general development area either passively or actively depending on the gassing regime, as described in Sections 6.1 and 6.2.
2. Secondary measure: venting beneath buildings, either passive or active measures depending on the gassing regime, as described in Sections 7.1 and 7.2.
3. Tertiary measure: a membrane installed within or below the building to provide a low-permeability barrier against methane ingress, as described in Section 8.

Examples of various methane gas-control systems are described throughout this report, see Sections 7.1.3, 7.2.2 and Box 32.

In contrast to methane, developments affected solely by carbon dioxide are not perceived as being immediately at risk. This is because even if a high concentration of carbon dioxide accumulates directly beneath a building, it does not pose an immediate risk to occupants, providing it is not allowed ingress. In these situations a gas-control system comprising only one or two individual protective measures could be sufficient. These measures might be:

1. Primary measure: passive venting beneath the building structure using a granular filled void to allow carbon dioxide to disperse, principally by diffusion (see Section 6.1).

2. Secondary measure: a membrane installed within or below the building to provide a low-permeability barrier against ingress of carbon dioxide (see Section 8).

Box 22 Example of gas-control system

At a former brickworks in the south east of England, desk study, ground investigation and analysis identified methane emanating from decomposing organic debris tipped into a system of old brick pits. It was proposed to develop the site as a business park, and four of nine two-storey office units were located over the infilled brick pits. Well constructed suspended ground slabs incorporating low-permeability gas membranes and a gas control system were installed based on passive venting beneath the office units. The passive venting was designed and installed in such a way that active venting by mechanical extraction of air could be incorporated if methane gas concentrations increased above acceptable levels. Prior to completion of the development, the concentration of methane gas under the units was monitored over several years. It was established that the passive venting was providing satisfactory dilution of air and that active venting using mechanical pumps did not have to be incorporated into the overall gas control system.

The type of development and usage is an important factor in the selection of individual protection measures. Residential housing is probably the most sensitive and more at risk from methane and associated gases. This is because of the difficulty of incorporating gas-control systems which:

*   should be effective for the design life of the building or until the gas regime ceases to be a hazard

*   need little or no maintenance

*   impose little or no infringement or constraint on the occupier's use of the property, including building modifications, land use, etc.

*   are energy efficient and incur little or no cost to run.

The above constraints limit the range of individual protective measures that are suitable. Their incorporation into a control system within the dwelling should be treated in a similar manner to the installation of damp proofing, thermal insulation or natural ventilation to buildings which require little or no maintenance.

The need to provide individual protection measures which require little or no maintenance has restricted gas-control systems for residential dwellings to predominantly passive venting together with the use of membranes (as discussed in Sections 7.1 and 8). However, passive venting is in turn limited to situations where adequate dilution of gas concentrations can be achieved by natural air movement (see Section 7.1) and this has restricted residential development to sites with low rates of gas emission.

In contrast, gas-control systems for commercial/retail development and offices, schools and public buildings can be installed and located in specific areas affording easy access for servicing and maintenance, e.g. service/mechanical plant rooms. This allows, therefore, more sophisticated gas-control systems to be used, e.g. incorporating individual protection measures such as active venting, controlled by gas monitoring equipment which constantly monitors the gas regime and air quality. By incorporating an element of flexibility in the design the initial gas-control system can be uprated or changed to suit changes in the gas regime at a later date or changes in the use or function of the building.

For the protection of buildings and structures from methane gas O'Riordan and Warren (1991) suggest that the range of measures in a gas-control system depend on type of development, gas regime and ground conditions as shown in Table 27.

Table 27 Gas-control systems to buildings for methane (after O'Riordan and Warren, 1991)

Gas-control system	Application
Well-constructed ground slab, possibly incorporating low-permeability membrane, no under slab void; creation of minimum number of enclosed spaces above slab; controlled venting of all spaces above ground slab.	Used for basements or where ground settlement unlikely or where methane gas emission rates are immeasurably low associated with ancient, natural organic materials (e.g. peat); mechanical ventilation systems can usually be adapted or extended.
Well-constructed ground slab, minimum number of penetrations of slab, passive or active venting beneath slab; blinding on surface of finished ground beneath building, low-permeability gas membrane either within slab or blinding layer.	Used where ground settlement is likely to continue and piled construction is necessary; also used where the building above does not have mechanical ventilation.
Well-constructed ground slab with active venting* beneath ground slab, minimum number of penetrations of slab, blinding on surface of finished ground, low-permeability gas membrane either within slab or blinding layer.	Used where methane concentrations and/or emission rates are expected to be unusually high and ventilation of the void alone might be insufficient to prevent accumulation of gas.

*   Active venting should be assumed to be necessary unless passive venting can be shown to be adequate by gas monitoring (see Sections 7.1, 7.2 and 9).

10.2   CURRENT GAS CONTROL PRACTICE

In order to establish current UK practices for gas control, over 100 case studies of development affected by gas were reviewed. Information about them was provided by the consultees from the organisations in Table 1, from published papers and from the in-house experience of the author's firm.

The case studies cover many types of development on a wide range of gassing regimes. Inevitably the information, known or made available, about the gassing regimes was limited. As a first basis of comparison, the case studies were sorted into those of new and of existing development and by considering three gas parameters as a means of characterising the gas regime in the ground. Table 28 presents the ranges of the gas parameter values used to distinguish six characteristic gassing situations. Note that the highest recorded (and reported) parameter, either methane or carbon dioxide concentration and/or emission rate, was taken as the determining factor of the characteristic situation of the development.

Table 28 Gassing parameters used to characterise case study situation

Gassing regime in ground			
Methane (% by volume in air)	Carbon dioxide (% by volume in air)	Emission rate[1] (m/s)	Characteristic situation[2]
<0.1	<1.5	Not detected	1
>0.1 – 1	>1.5 – 5	Not detected	2
>1 – 5	<5	Not detected	3
>5 – 20	<20	<0.01	4
>20	>20	>0.01 – 0.05	5
>20	>20	>0.05	6

Notes:

1. Emission rate values measured as equivalent total gas flow velocity from a 50 mm diameter borehole; for methods of measurement see Crowhurst and Manchester (1992).

2. Highest measured parameter used as determining factor.

Table 29 Gas-control systems for new development: current UK practice

Characteristic situation[1]	Residential housing[2]	Office/commercial[2] including multi-storey dwellings
1	No special precautions.	No special precautions.
2	a, b, c and d.	a, b, c and d.
3	a, b, c, d and i, and possibly h.	a, b, c, d and i.
4	a, b, c, d, f, g and possibly k.	a, b, c, d, f, and j.
5	Reduce gas regime prior to development using e and f or g, confirm risk level by k.	a, b, c, d, g, h and k.
6	Reduce gas regime prior to development using e and g; possibly consider gas utilisation; confirm risk level by k.	Not appropriate; reduce gas regime prior to development using e and f or g; confirm risk level by k.

Notes:

1. Characteristic situation as described in Table 28

2. Range of gas protection measures as follows:

a	ventilation of confined spaces within building	g	active in-ground venting
b	well-constructed ground slab	h	passive venting to building – underslab void
c	low-permeability gas membrane	i	passive venting to building – granular filled void
d	minimum penetration of ground slab by services	j	active venting to building
e	in-ground barrier	k	gas monitoring of installed measures with alarms.
f	passive in-ground venting		

In terms of these characteristic gas situations, Tables 29 and 30 show the measures used for gas control in current UK practice for new and existing development respectively. From the reviewed case studies and discussions with designers and practitioners it would appear that it is rare for any gas-control system not to perform adequately at least in the sense that for most cases there have been no reports of subsequent problems. In very few cases is there confirmation by a properly managed and quantitative design audit on the performance of the system using gas monitoring data.

Table 30 Gas-control systems for existing development: current UK practice

Characteristic situation[1]	Residential housing[2]	Office/commercial[2] including multi-storey dwellings
1	No special precautions.	No special precautions.
2	a and k.	a and k.
3	a, k and f.	a, k and f.
4	a, k, e and f possibly i.	a, k, e and f, possibly g using portable equipment.
5	a, k, e, f or g.	a, k, e, f or g.
6	Consider evacuation, a, k, e and g.	Consider evacuation, a, k, e and g.

Notes:

1. Characteristic situation as described in Table 28
2. Range of gas protection measures as follows:

a	ventilation of confined spaces within building	g	active in-ground venting
b	well-constructed ground slab	h	passive venting to building – underslab void
c	low-permeability gas membrane	i	passive venting to building – granular filled void
d	minimum penetration of ground slab by services	j	active venting to building
e	in-ground barrier	k	gas monitoring of installed measures with alarms.
f	passive in-ground venting		

11 Protection to existing development

The findings of this report indicate that the incidence of existing development being affected by gassing ground is widespread throughout the UK. Landfill gas and mine gas would appear to be the major sources of methane and carbon dioxide affecting existing development. Incidents involving methane gas explosions in existing development have been recorded by Baker (1987), Clow (1991) and Jaitly (1987). Recorded instances of existing development affected by methane and associated gases from other sources, such as natural organic deposits, sewers, etc., are not common. The various sources of methane and associated gases are discussed in Section 2.1.

The application of gas protection measures to existing development is constrained by the following factors:

- difficult access, particularly in urban areas or to land in private ownership
- existing infrastructure, e.g. buried utility services, may have to be diverted or incorporated into in-ground gas protection measures
- protection measures to buildings cannot easily be incorporated without major disruption both to the structure and occupants.

Furthermore, existing development affected by gassing ground tends to involve several or many buildings over a considerable area rather than a single building. For these reasons the approach adopted to existing development is usually to remove or isolate the gassing source rather than attempt to protect individual buildings. Only if removal or isolation of the gassing source cannot be undertaken for practical or economic reasons should protection measures to individual buildings be considered.

11.1 IN-GROUND PROTECTION MEASURES

Isolation of the gassing source can be carried out using in-ground barriers and venting techniques as described in Sections 5 and 6 respectively. In certain situations removal of the gassing ground may be possible. These techniques and their applications are reviewed below.

Excavation and disposal

This technique is applicable where the gassing source can be readily identified and excavated, subject to the limitations discussed in Section 4.2 particularly associated with the safe disposal of gassing material. Costs for disposal of large volumes of material can be high. Excavation and disposal can have particular applications and benefits in connection with mine gas from coal workings. In favourable circumstances excavation of the gassing source can be undertaken as part of opencast coal mining operations. The gassing coal seam or seams are removed from the opencast working and the non-gassing spoil material replaced and compacted (see Box 23).

In-ground barriers in conjunction with passive venting

In-ground barriers in conjunction with passive in-ground venting have been widely used in the UK to protect large areas of existing development from gas migration. In most applications vertical barriers have been used to intercept lateral gas migration from landfill affecting adjacent existing development. Two examples of the use of these techniques are described in Boxes 24 and 25.

Box 23 Example of gas protection by excavation and disposal

At Arkwright Town in Derbyshire, many existing residential houses had been affected by mine gas from coal workings beneath the village. Mining subsidence beneath the village had caused the ground to fracture and become more permeable, allowing methane to rise to the ground surface from both shallow and deep abandoned coal workings. Gas burning in a fire grate within one house had been identified as methane in excess of 1% by volume in air migrating from the underlying mine workings. The highest methane concentration was 17% by volume in air recorded from a sample of gas extracted through an air brick set in a house wall. A decision has been taken by British Coal in conjunction with the local authority to move and rebuild the village on an adjacent development site free from the risk of gas arising from the coal workings. In parallel with this, the shallow coal seams beneath the existing village are to be excavated by opencast methods and the spoil replaced. Thereafter the site will be restored and re-landscaped and returned to agricultural use.

The capital cost of the new village development will be offset by revenue from coal gained from the opencast operations and reworking of the old Arkwright Colliery spoil tips. The opencast activity is expected to yield some four million tonnes of coal over a period of 10 years.

Box 24 Protection to existing development using in-ground techniques: case study 1

At a site near Sandwell in the West Midlands, a vertical in-ground barrier has been installed to prevent landfill gas migration from an adjacent former landfill site. The landfill was within an old marl pit and some 20 m deep. Landfill gas migration was through the permeable sand and gravel stratum overlying the marls/clays. Variable methane and carbon dioxide concentrations of 48 to 76% and 11 to 29% by volume in air respectively were measured. Existing residential housing was located some 20 m to 30 m from the edge of the landfill boundary. A vertical in-ground barrier has been designed comprising a synthetic HDPE liner installed within a self-hardening bentonite/cement cut-off. Details of these types of barrier systems are given in Section 5.6. At this particular site the barrier was designed not only to prevent gas migration but also to offer minimal obstruction to groundwater flow which is predominantly through the sand and gravel stratum normal to the barrier. This is because there was general concern that the construction of a deep cut-off barrier 'keyed' into the underlying low-permeability marls and clays would have an impounding effect on groundwater flow. This would result in water level rises in the sand and gravel upstream of the cut-off barrier and underneath the existing houses which were already in poor condition. Any increase in groundwater level might reduce the bearing capacity of the soil and affect foundation stability of the houses. For this reason the barrier was designed to extend only 1 to 2 m depth below the lowest recorded groundwater level within the sand and gravel stratum. Thus the groundwater flow would still continue beneath the barrier in the sand and gravel. Lateral gas migration would be protected by the barrier itself and the groundwater table. The depth of the barrier ranged between 5 and 7 m and was constructed over a length of some 700 m. Other protection measures include a granular filled vent trench (see Section 6.1.2) about 15 m behind the in-ground barrier on the landfill side to an average depth of 4 m. Between the vent trench and the in-ground barrier, gas venting wells (see Section 6.1.2) were installed at a 50-m spacing. The vent trench was installed to the depth of the water table. The gas wells were about 30 m deep, i.e. into the underlying marl/clay to intercept and vent any possible landfill gas migrating at depth.

At an old landfill site near Oldbury in the West Midlands, landfill gas migration was identified from the site through made ground at shallow depth and through permeable sandstone bands within the Etruria Marl at depth. Methane and carbon dioxide concentrations of some 40% to 60% and 20% to 30% by volume in air respectively were monitored from the landfill site. Landfill gas was detected in existing residential properties on the opposite side of the road from the landfill site. To prevent further lateral migration of landfill gas a synthetic barrier was installed within a granular venting trench constructed along the boundary of the tip opposite the affected properties (see Sections 5.4 and 6.1.2). The synthetic barrier comprised an HDPE liner, 2.5-mm thick, 4-m deep and keyed at least 0.5 m into the Marl. The total length of barrier was 208 m.

Details of the installed barrier are shown in the figure below. To ensure adequate drainage and to minimise maintenance the HDPE liner was laid against a permeable fin drain which in turn was backed by a geotextile filter material to prevent ingress of fines. The base of the trench was laid to falls so that surface water infiltration into the fin drain would flow to the lower end of the trench where it would discharge into natural ground. The venting trench itself was 0.8-m wide and filled with granular material of 10 to 100 mm nominal size.

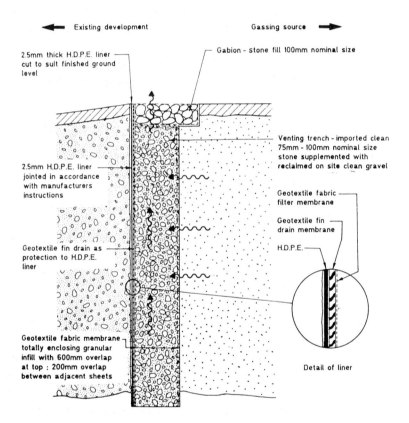

Monitoring the landfill gas levels after installation of the in-ground barrier and venting trench indicated a reduction in methane concentrations to 20% by volume in air within the landfill and to 1 to 2% by volume in air beyond the barrier over a 6 to 9 month period. However, installation of these protection measures appeared to have little effect on carbon dioxide concentrations which remained approximately at their original levels. This is believed to be because of changes in the landfill gas production regime as a direct result of the installation of the venting trench allowing oxidation of methane to carbon dioxide in aerobic conditions (see Section 2.2).

Active in-ground abstraction

Active in-ground abstraction in the UK has been applied to the protection of existing development particularly to address the problems of gas migration from landfill and abandoned shallow mine workings. The principle and application of this technique is discussed in Section 6.2.3, with examples of its use described in Box 12.

A variation of active in-ground abstraction is described by Manley *et al.*(1991) for gas protection to existing development. This method relies upon the simultaneous abstraction of the hazardous gas from the ground on one side of the development or building and its replacement by injecting inert gas into the ground along the opposite side to form an inert buffer zone beneath the building. This method has been used at a site near Belfast, Northern Ireland, to protect an existing commercial development built directly on landfill. Landfill gas is extracted from a network of horizontal collector pipes and delivered *via* a collector ring main and an abstraction pump to a combustion chamber which burns the gas. The resultant exhaust gas is predominantly nitrogen, carbon dioxide and water vapour. This exhaust gas is returned to the ground through a separate distribution pipework system and individual injector pipes.

In North America the use of active in-ground abstraction has been applied to new and existing development, particularly existing subsurface development (see Section 12.3).

11.2 PROTECTION MEASURES TO BUILDINGS

In certain circumstances in-ground protection measures will not be sufficient to prevent gas migration affecting existing development and individual dwellings. This is particularly the case where gas is migrating vertically upwards below the development and cannot be effectively intercepted on a horizontal plane using in-ground barriers or be vented by in-ground ventilation, e.g. gas migrating from disused coal mine workings *via* shafts as discussed in Section 2.2. In such situations gas protection measures to individual existing buildings and structures will be necessary to prevent gas ingress into the building.

The hazards and effects of gas ingress within buildings are discussed in Section 2.4. In principle there are two methods of providing gas protection. These are:

1. Using membranes to prevent infiltration of methane and associated gases into an existing building *via* ground floor, below-ground walls and all service entry points. Gas protection measures for substructures are discussed in Section 12.3 and protection to service entry points is described in Section 12.2.

2. Using passive or active venting techniques to buildings (see Sections 7.1, 7.2 and 12.3.3) to dilute and disperse gas in order to prevent increases in gas concentrations and pressures. In this way gas ingress *via* cracks or openings in the building fabric can be prevented (see Section 2.3).

There are several factors which call for a different approach when protecting existing rather than new buildings from the ingress of methane and associated gases. This is because the protection measures that can be applied effectively are limited by constraints such as building structural, access, dissruption of use, and uncertainty about the points of gas entry.

Building structure

The structural and foundation layout of the existing building will limit the installation and positioning of both membranes and ventilation measures. Protection measures have to accommodate structure details such as upstanding/downstanding beams, columns, changes in slab level, etc. This becomes increasingly difficult with the complexity of the building layout at or below ground level. Another important aspect is that it is essential that any form of gas protection measure that is installed does not compromise the operation of existing buildings/structure details such as protection against water or damp ingress, thermal insulation, interior air quality (i.e. natural ventilation and humidity). For example, sealing of timber floors using in-structure membranes to prevent gas ingress can result in dry rot if natural ventilation is inhibited.

Access and disruption

In many existing buildings, installation of low-permeability gas membranes or passive or active ventilation measures would involve severe difficulties of working access. For example, with a building with a ground-bearing slab, it would be extremely difficult to provide passive or active ventilation beneath the slab as described in Sections 7.1 or 7.2 because of gaining access. Excavation beneath the building could result in structural distress of the ground slab, i.e. further cracking creating more potential openings to the ingress of gas. In addition, buried services may also hinder access. A further difficulty is the severe disruption to occupants of the building. Such disruption may not be tolerated, e.g. if residents or staff had to be moved out and re-located temporarily while the protection measures were installed. A case study of providing a form of underslab venting to existing residential development is described in Box 26.

Identification of gas entry points

The detection of gas within a building can be identified and confirmed using portable or permanently installed gas monitoring equipment (see Section 9). Less certain, however, is the identification of all gas entry routes into the building. Failing to seal relatively minor openings will compromise any protection measure installed. For this reason in older buildings, extensive barrier and sealing protection measures may be needed to prevent gas ingress. In older buildings it may not be technically feasible to apply extensive barriers and sealing protection measures except by so reducing the natural ventilation and air circulation within the structure that it would result in humidity and condensation problems.

In view of the difficulties of applying gas protection measures and the increased risk of not identifying or not being able to seal all gas entry routes, it is good practice to adopt gas-control systems which combine both in-ground and building gas protection measures. The use of gas-control systems in these situations is discussed in Section 10.

An important component of the gas-control system would be the provision of gas monitoring and alarm equipment. A description of the use and application of gas monitoring and alarm equipment is given in Section 9. Within an existing building, such equipment is particularly useful because:

1. It enables the gas protection measures that are installed to be monitored and their reliability or otherwise in preventing gas ingress to be identified.

2. Permanent gas sensors in critical/sensitive parts of the building (i.e. confined spaces, false ceilings, service chambers or ducts) enable regular checks of air quality and, if gas is detected, the need for additional gas protection measures can be considered.

3. It allows continued use of the existing building by occupants while gas concentrations are within acceptable levels. In contrast, if no gas monitoring is undertaken and there is a risk to occupants, the safest course of action, in the absence of information on gas concentrations, might be to evacuate the building.

This may be the case for existing residential development where the risk to owners/occupiers is perceived to be high.

Box 26 Passive venting beneath existing buildings

Passive venting can be installed beneath existing development. The general technique is to drive horizontal or inclined bores using temporary casing beneath the ground slab. As the casing is withdrawn the resulting void is filled with granular material and/or slotted pipework to form a gas well. A series of such wells will provide partial venting beneath the ground slab as shown in the figure below. The principle of operation and design is similar to that for a gas venting well as described in Section 6.1.2. Incorporation of slotted pipework allows the use of active venting techniques should passive venting not adequately dilute and disperse the gas. Installation of the casing can be either by conventional drilling or jacking techniques depending on the diameter of the well and its inclination. A longitudinal venting trench collects gas vented from the pipework and allows it to disperse to atmosphere. Alternatively, individual wells can be vented via a manifold duct and a vent stack as shown in figure(b) below. This latter arrangement has been used to provide passive venting to a residential development in the Midlands affected by landfill gas.

In view of the difficulties of gaining adequate access for necessary plant and equipment and the relatively high capital cost, the technique has been limited to providing passive venting beneath small and single buildings such as houses and substructures such as basements. When using this technique care should be taken to minimise ground disturbance during installation of the wells to prevent movement and subsidence of the building.

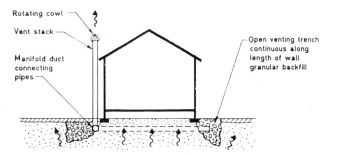

(a) Horizontal pipework beneath structure surrounded in granular material either connected to open venting trench or vent stack via manifold

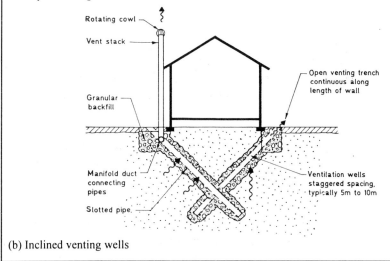

(b) Inclined venting wells

Examples of various gas-control systems applied to existing development buildings, which include protection measures to buildings/structures, are outlined in Boxes 26 and 27.

Box 27 Protection to existing industrial and leisure development

A ground investigation carried out in an existing developed area of landfill reclamation identified landfill gas affecting an industrial building and leisure centre. The investigation involved establishing a series of monitoring points in boreholes surrounding the development and within the buildings/structures. High levels of methane, above 5% by volume in air, were detected in the ground surrounding the development. Both buildings were naturally well-ventilated and no significant concentrations of methane or associated gases were detected. However, high methane levels were found in a service duct in one building. Although adequate dilution and dispersion of the gas was occurring within the buildings themselves, this situation could not be guaranteed to be maintained, particularly if there was a future change in use of the buildings such as to reduce the current well-ventilated environment. Gas-protection measures were therefore considered to be necessary. In order to allow continued use of the buildings and to minimise disruption to the occupants, it was agreed with the local authority to implement the following gas-control system:

- passive in-ground venting using granular filled venting trenches to surround and isolate the more highly gassing areas

- permanent gas monitoring and alarm equipment within buildings to provide an effective safeguard to warn of any future increase in methane concentrations.

Gas monitoring and alarm equipment was thought to be particularly appropriate because the limited access between buildings meant that the venting trench could not be installed to surround completely all of the areas of gassing ground. Gas sensors were located within the existing buildings, particularly in those areas not surrounded by the venting trench. An in-place sensor system was used to record gas concentrations (see Section 9.2). Sensors were located in specific locations, around service entry points and confined or poorly ventilated spaces, e.g. storeroom, cupboards, WCs, etc. A two-stage audible alarm was incorporated into the gas monitoring equipment which had a low level warning with intermittent audible alarm set at a methane concentration of 0.5% by volume in air and a high level continuous audible warning set at a methane concentration of 1% by volume in air for evacuation of personnel.

The use of permanent gas monitoring and alarm equipment has proved to be extremely effective in confirming the adequacy and performance of the passive in-ground venting measures. There has been no incident of the alarm being triggered other than at times of routine testing and maintenance. It has enabled continued use of the existing buildings with increased security and confidence.

11.3 EFFECT OF BUILDING MODIFICATIONS

Building modifications include extensions and structural alterations as well as home repairs and improvements. Modifications can result in:

- breaching the continuity of a gas-protection measure allowing direct gas entry into a development or building

- impairing or preventing natural fresh air supply to passive or active venting measures resulting in inadequate dilution and dispersion of gas

- changing gassing regime within the ground.

The design and installation of gas-protection measures have to be development specific. For this reason any subsequent building modification or addition may impair their efficacy and operation. Building modifications may also disrupt in-ground gas protection measures such as barriers, passive venting and active abstraction systems. Failures to these types of measures can occur where they may be breached by foundations or service trenches for new structures. An example of this is outlined in Box 28.

Box 28 Gas protection measures affected by building modifications

A residential development in Kent, constructed in four phases, is situated adjacent to a former landfill. A consultant was appointed by the developer to engineer the development including the design of the gas-control system to protect the whole site area and the initial phase of two-storey housing. The gas-control system comprised three components as follows:

1. A perimeter venting trench with an HDPE in-ground barrier on the site boundary adjacent to the landfill, covered and vented at specific locations via vent stacks

2. A passive venting system beneath the houses, which were founded on conventional shallow footings with suspended ground slabs and underslab void

3. A gas monitoring/alarm system attached to pipework within the open underfloor void.

The gas-control system to this initial design worked satisfactorily with no landfill gas detected. Some 18 months after completion of the first phase of development, the original developer sold the remaining areas of the site, together with details and drawings of the gas-control system to a second developer who employed another consultant to undertake the engineering design work including any appropriate gas-control systems.

These three remaining phases were three and four-storey residential dwellings which, because of the structural loading/ground conditions, had to be founded on driven piles. Installation of driven piles for the buildings close to the anticipated position of the existing perimeter venting trench caused excessive ground movement and breached the integrity of the synthetic liner allowing landfill gas to migrate into the development. This triggered the gas alarm in the first-phase residential houses. On investigation, several piles were found to have been installed along the line of the trench which was not in position as shown on the original drawings.

The venting trench and synthetic liner were reinstated in their as-constructed location. The piling layout of the remaining buildings was amended which necessitated the use of cantilevered ground beams to prevent breaching the perimeter vent trench and in-ground barrier elsewhere on the site.

Existing buildings which incorporate a gas-control system based on passive or active venting can be particularly affected by construction of building extensions or alterations which change the external flow of air around the building. This is because the building extension will deflect the wind force acting on the structure as a whole. This may reduce both the pressure exerted on the windward side affording air inlet action and the suction on the leeward side where wall vents act as outlets for exhaust air and gas. The magnitude of the effect on the original gas-control system will depend on the height and length of the building extension. Changes in wind force and pressure distribution around buildings of various height, shape and width can be estimated from CP3: Section V: Part 2 (BSI, 1972) and Digests 141 and 346 (BRE, 1982 and 1989). The provision of shelter from the wind force also allows more effective action of the 'stack effect' (see Section 7.1), although this is seen to be generally very small in relation to actual changes in wind pressures, except in the case of tall buildings.

Building modifications and extensions may also influence the action of passive or active venting systems beneath an adjacent building or in-ground venting system, because of changes in windforce distribution as shown in Figure 46. The conditions in the surroundings will modify these effects. In dense city areas with many tall buildings, the extremes of wind force and speed may be many times greater than those based on design tables for wind load. Calculation of these effects on a large development or building is not always possible and wind tunnel model tests may have to be undertaken to aid design of a gas-control system which relies on passive ventilation of buildings.

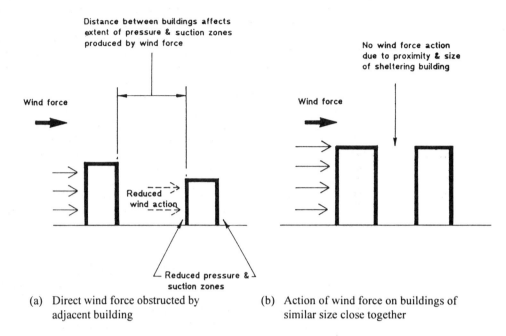

(a) Direct wind force obstructed by adjacent building

(b) Action of wind force on buildings of similar size close together

Figure 46 Distribution of wind pressures from adjacent buildings

Thus when designing a building extension or modification it is necessary to check the design of the original gas-control system for the effects of changes in volume flow rate of fresh air supply, particularly in the case of passive venting measures. Section 7.1.1 discusses the principles of design of passive venting for buildings. In cases where the efficacy of the gas-control system is potentially reduced additional measures should be undertaken to maintain effectiveness. For existing buildings which rely on passive venting measures for gas protection this may be difficult if structural alterations to the original building are needed, e.g. installation of additional air vents to underfloor voids. Even if practicable to do so, there would be major disruption for occupants, particularly in residential housing. In these circumstances it may be more effective to prevent or limit the extent of the building of extensions or structural alterations.

Gas-control systems incorporating active venting can be altered more easily to cope with building modifications. In these situations any increase in air flow rates required to the venting system can be undertaken by up-rating the mechanical components, rather than by any fundamental changes to the layout of void space or sizing of pipework, etc. For this reason active venting has advantages over passive venting since it is more adaptable to changes in usage of a building (see Sections 7.1.3 and 7.2.2).

Extensions to existing buildings may also result in an increase in gas emission from the ground which may reduce the efficacy of a gas-control system, if initially installed. Case studies of existing development affected by gassing ground and subsequently modified are outlined in Boxes 29 and 30.

Box 29 Existing housing affected by building extension

A residential development in an urban environment in the north-west of England had for many years slowly encroached on an area of derelict land which had been used for tipping domestic household waste. A single-storey extension in the rear garden to a house was granted planning permission by the local authority. The building control officer required strip footings to the extension and that they should be 0.15-m deeper than the existing house foundations, a total of some 1-m. The base of the excavations for the extension exposed domestic household waste which on further inspection was found to be gassing with levels of methane up to 10% by volume in air. No gas was detected within or beneath the existing house. Indeed there was no visible indication in the rear garden of landfill gas emission, e.g. die back of vegetation. The extension was constructed on piled foundations with a suspended concrete ground slab and a gas-control system was installed which comprised passive ventilation using an open underfloor void. An HDPE low-permeability membrane was laid within the ground slab beneath a concrete screed. In addition, a venting trench 5-m deep to the base of the landfill was installed on the boundary of the rear garden. No gas protection measures were undertaken to the original house except periodic monitoring using portable instruments to check on the possible ingress of landfill gas.

A similar example occurred in the south east of England where a single-storey extension to the rear of an existing house was constructed partly over gassing filled ground. In view of the presence of fill the house has partly piled foundations; and because of the potential risk of landfill gas emission from the ground also incorporated were passive venting beneath the ground slab and a low-permeability gas membrane (comprising a composite aluminium foil/HDPE carrier within the slab). Similar precautions against landfill gas were taken for the extension except that it was constructed using conventional strip footings. Very soon after construction differential settlement between the extension and house led to structural cracking and rotation of the extension away from the house. This movement resulted in rupture of the gas membrane within the concrete ground slab and ingress of landfill gas into the building resulting in odour problems. The extension was underpinned and external cracks made good with a gas-resistant flexible sealant. The damaged membrane was repaired by laying a strip of similar material over the area of rupture and sealing with bitumen. The concrete screed was then reinstated.

Box 30 Warehouse development affected by change of use

In addition to modifications to the building structure, changes in use of the existing development and implications on gas protection should also be considered. At a site near Cwmbran, Gwent, a warehouse development was constructed on a former refuse tip founded on dynamically consolidated material (Downie and Treharne, 1979). The development, completed in the mid-1970s, incorporated a granular blanket to provide passive venting of any landfill gas, beneath a ground-bearing concrete slab. In the early 1980s landfill gas and associated odours were detected in one building. The ingress of the gas was found to be coming from cracks/joints in the floor slab. An investigation into the problem indicated that a change in use of the warehouse had resulted in higher loading intensity on the ground slab which in turn resulted in foundation settlement and opening of construction joints and cracks. Given that the warehouse was relatively large and naturally well ventilated it was considered necessary only to re-seal cracks and joints with a suitable mastic sealant. The problem has not reoccurred.

12 Services and substructures

12.1 IN GROUND PROTECTION TO SERVICES

All development will require services of some kind depending on usage, i.e. mains gas, electricity, foul and surface water drainage, etc. Most services will be installed below ground in service trenches (possibly in ducts in the case of electricity or telephone cables). Buried services and their points of entry into buildings provide potential pathways for methane and associated gases in the ground to migrate into development or buildings. These migration pathways and entry routes are discussed in Section 2.3.

Services are usually laid in wide oversized trenches and bedded on free draining material. Above the bedding material the trench is backfilled with selected inert granular material for ease of compaction to prevent differential settlement of the pipe or duct. Useful guidance on material selection for backfilling to trenches is given in BS 8301:1985 and Volume 1, Series 500 of the *Manual of Contract Documents for Highway Works* prepared by the DTp (1991). In contaminated ground the use of inert granular backfill is particularly important to prevent corrosion of pipework and to allow re-excavation by maintenance staff without risk of exposure to contaminants. The granular bedding and backfill materials used are likely to be more permeable than the surrounding ground. Thus in gassing ground the service trench may tend to act as a passive venting trench or gas drain and encourage gas to migrate and possibly collect within it (venting trenches and gas drains are discussed in Section 6.1.2). This can result in gas migrating through the permeable backfill of the trench directly to the service entry point in the building. Campbell (1987) gives an account of an incident where landfill gas was identified as migrating into an existing sewer pipe trench being excavated to provide services to a new housing development some 30 m from a landfill site boundary.

A general difficulty with the provision of services on gassing ground is the achievement of enough flexibility in ducts or service pipes to accommodate the effects of ground movement and differential settlement. This is a particular problem on gassing ground associated with landfill or mining where the ground movement may be ongoing. On gassing landfill, settlement from organic degradation can be expected to be as much as 20% of the fill thickness (O'Riordan and Warren, 1991 and Leach and Goodger, 1991). In these circumstances, sufficient flexibility should be provided to services and entry points to buildings in order to prevent distortion and possible rupture of the duct or pipe or seal that would otherwise allow ingress of gas.

Gas migration *via* a service trench can be prevented by the use of vertical in-ground barriers. A barrier is constructed across the service trench (usually perpendicular to the trench) and the service pipe or duct is surrounded and sealed with compacted clay, as shown in Figure 47(a). Section 5.4 describes the requirements and properties of clay materials to form low-permeability in-ground barriers. In most cases the vertical in-ground barrier across the service trench can also be part of a much larger barrier system installed to prevent general gas migration affecting development. In these situations the clay barrier across the service trench is keyed into the general barrier system.

When sealing service pipes or ducts which penetrate vertical barriers formed from synthetic and/or bentonite slurry, it is usual to provide special preformed sections of liner, termed cloaks, which are attached and sealed with mastic to the pipe and then welded to adjacent panels of synthetic barrier. Typical details of special preformed sections manufactured to accommodate services are shown in Figure 47(b).

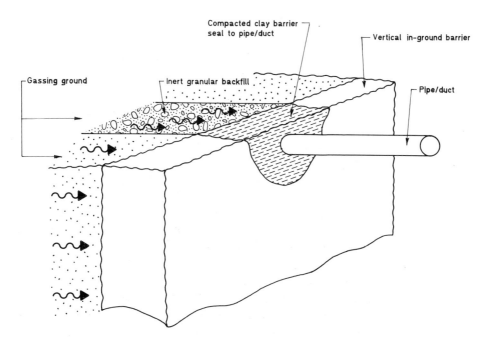

(a) Clay barrier seal to service trench and pipe

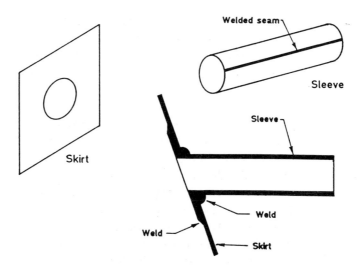

(b) Preformed seal to service pipe or duct passing through synthetic barrier

Figure 47 In-ground gas protection to services

In situations where a vertical in-ground barrier is not present, gas migration into a service trench can be prevented by re-routing all services into a purpose-built culvert made gas resistant either by fixing a low-permeability synthetic liner externally to the culvert or by incorporating a structural synthetic membrane within it. Details of these products and methods of installation are discussed in Sections 5.5 and 8.1.2 respectively.

12.2　　PROTECTION AT SERVICE ENTRY POINTS

Service entry points at or below ground level also provide potential areas of gas ingress from the ground into a building (see also Section 2.3). Ingress of natural gas from leaking or fractured pipe mains into telecommunication buildings and chambers *via* unsealed service ducts has been responsible for a number of gas explosions in the recent past (PSA, 1977). Furthermore, plastic pipework used for service ducting (including some jointing compounds and sealants) can be permeable to methane and associated gases over a long exposure period resulting in gas ingress into the service duct itself.

Normal practice is to bring service utilities to a building within a duct or pipe. These are usually laid by the developer below ground when groundworks are being carried out. Guidelines for the provision of utility services to building development are given in publications Nos 2, 5, 6 and 7 prepared by the NJUG (1979, 1983, 1984 and 1986). General building practice is for services to enter above foundation/footing level and through the ground slab or cavity wall. The reasons for this practice are to protect individual services from:

- accidental damage by the occupants of the building which could occur if the surfaces were left exposed on the external walls

- the effects of frost and ice, particularly in the case of water supply.

Foul drainage is also routed in this way as it is very often the only means of providing adequate falls to pipe runs. Gas service pipes are the exception to the above which in accordance with the Gas Safety (Installation and Use) Regulations (1974) must not be routed through unventilated voids or beneath load bearing footings or foundations. The gas service pipe is instead brought to a terminal or meter box attached to an external wall of the building (British Gas, 1990).

The general practice adopted for service utilities and foul drainage does not accord with the principles of gas protection which are to minimise or prevent any disruption to the integrity of the ground slab or cavity wall. The principle used to prevent ingress at service entry points into buildings is that of using barriers to resist ingress and venting to encourage dispersion and dilution. In many situations utility services and ducts can be re-routed so that they enter the building from the outside wall above foundation ground slab level in a similar manner to that adopted for the normal installation of gas service pipes. This avoids the need to create an entry point through the ground slab or cavity wall. Typical details of external service entries and ducting designed to prevent gas ingress into a building are shown in Figure 48.

Rys and Johns (1985) describe the construction of an office/commercial development on gassing ground where all services were brought to specially designed and ventilated structures located on the outside of the buildings. The structures were designed to be an architectural feature of the buildings (see Figure 49).

In certain situations the provision of external service entry points above the ground slab cannot be undertaken without constraining the development layout. An example is the difficulty of providing foul drains with adequate falls. Where penetration of a ground slab is unavoidable a gas membrane across the ground slab (either attached below or over the slab) is an essential requirement for gas protection (see Section 8). This method is used because of the difficulty of providing adequate seals between the ducts or services and the ground slab as explained in Section 8. Sealing the service or duct to the membrane depends on the materials to be joined. In the case of LDPE and HDPE membranes this can be achieved by welding (heat bonding) between the membrane and the service pipe or duct using a mastic or modified bitumen polymer sealant. In these situations, however, the service pipe or duct has to be heat resistant to avoid being damaged.

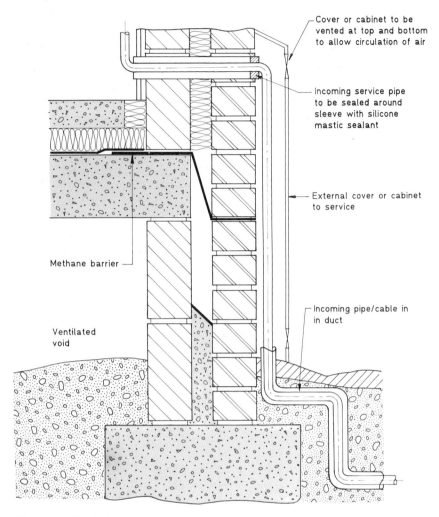

Figure 48 Typical gas protection measures to service entry points

Composite synthetic membranes which incorporate an aluminium sheet component that provides a low permeability to gas cannot easily be welded or sealed by this technique. In this case the aluminium sheet has to be continuous, fully covering the plan area of the building. Multi-layers of membrane might be required to provide an integral seal over the entire plan area.

Service entry pipes or ducts can be sealed by the use of preformed sections of membrane (sometimes also known as top hats or collars) which are fitted over or around the protruding pipe or duct and sealed to the membrane either by welding or heat bonding. The preformed section is similarly sealed to the base of the pipe or duct. A jubilee clip can be used to secure the top of the preformed section to the pipe or duct. Figure 50 shows typical preformed sections of membranes used to seal service entries through ground slabs.

Figure 51 shows an example of finished drainage pipework sealed to the structural membrane. Where a service duct is eventually to carry smaller diameter pipe work or cable the duct can be cut at membrane level and a special membrane section fitted across the duct with a hole to accommodate the smaller pipe or cable. The membrane can then be fitted over or around the pipe or cable and the small gap sealed with a gas-resistant sealant tape or adhesive material.

Figure 49 Ventilated external service entry points

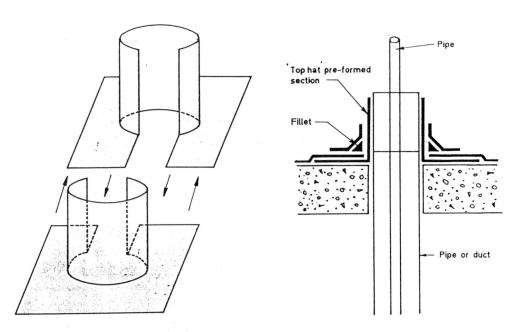

(a) Typical collar or 'top hat' preformed section for sealing service pipes or ducts

(b) Typical arrangement of bonding collar to low permeability gas membrane across ground slab

Figure 50 Preformed membrane sections for service entry points

Figure 51 Drainage pipework sealed to membrane

Figure 52 Example of where grouping of services can cause difficulties in sealing
membrane across ground slab

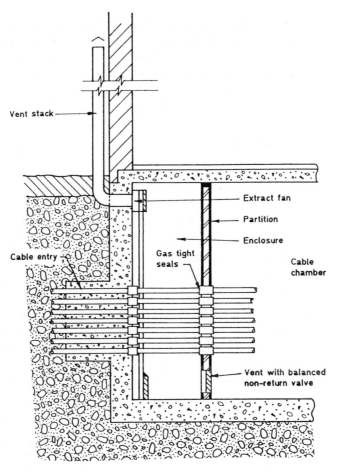

Figure 53 Example of active venting to substructure duct seal

Having to seal large groups of services can make installation of preformed membrane sections difficult and should be avoided if at all possible (see Figure 52). A practice has developed of installing services through the external wall below ground level and taking them up the cavity formed between the external and internal walls above ground-slab level. This practice should be avoided also because of the difficulty of making a permanent and durable seal where the service penetrates the dpc or cavity tray and gas membrane.

Service entries into substructures, such as service basements or cable chambers, have particular design needs for gas protection (see Section 12.3). This is because although the point of entry of the service pipe or duct can be sealed in the wall or floor of the substructure there is not always the opportunity to provide adequate venting and dispersion if gas should enter. In these circumstances mechanical ventilation can be provided to specific duct enclosures as shown in Figure 53.

12.3   PROTECTION TO SUBSURFACE DEVELOPMENTS

Subsurface development can be defined as any form of construction which is built entirely or partially below ground level (including development constructed in cut on sloping ground). The structure will usually be part of an above-ground development, e.g. a basement or cellar or undercroft to a multi-storey development, or it may be constructed as a single stand-alone structure entirely or partially below ground level, e.g. underground service chamber and connecting tunnels.

Subsurface development is particularly vulnerable to the hazards of gas migration from the ground. Investigations into fires and explosions which occurred during the 1960s and 1970s in telecommunication exchange buildings identified that gas ingress into associated subsurface basements and service chambers was the prime cause. Many incidents of explosions stemmed from gas migration from nearby leaking town gas supply pipes (PSA, 1977 and Clow, 1991).

The factors listed below are of particular importance in defining the problems for subsurface development:

1. Much of the surface area of the substructure can be in direct contact with the gassing ground, i.e. floor, walls and possibly roof. The relatively high surface area exposed to gas increases the risk of entry routes to gas ingress.

2. The general lack of openings in substructures direct to the atmosphere, e.g. windows and doors, means that natural ventilation within it will be limited and may not be sufficient to dilute or disperse gas which may enter from external ground source.

3. Provision of adequate natural ventilation and possibly heating for habitable development may result in a lower air pressure within the structure relative to surrounding atmosphere and gas within the ground. Should there be an entry route into the substructure, gas will be encouraged to migrate from the surrounding ground under a pressure gradient by the process of advection (see also Section 2.2).

4. As there is direct contact between the subsurface development and the ground, gas can migrate by the process of diffusion. This process may be immaterial in small subsurface developments located in ground with low gas concentrations, but it may be significant in a large substructure, such as a deep multi-storey basement with large floor area constructed in ground with high concentrations of gas.

5. In deep subsurface development, soil or groundwater pressures may give rise to associated high gas pressures as well as gas in solution (see Section 2.2). This can create problems such as:

    - release of high concentration or flow of gas into excavations during construction creating hazards such as unsafe working conditions

    - defects in construction, e.g. formation of gas pockets in freshly placed concrete piles or diaphragm walls causing structural deterioration

    - gas ingress through fabric of the substructure.

In many deep basements, the design of the lowest basement slab requires control of underlying water pressures using permanent pumping. Drainage cavities are often placed inside perimeter retaining walls. When detailing these elements, care is needed to avoid their acting as traps for gases released from solution into the permanent drainage system.

Given the difficulties listed above, design and construction of subsurface development should aim to minimise the possibility of gas entry, e.g:

- openings in the floor or walls of any substructure should be kept to a minimum

- procedures should be adopted to limit construction joints and control cracking in all masonry and concrete elements (see Section 4.2).

The use of steel reinforcement, special concrete mixes, additives, proper curing and design of control joints to reduce the frequency of cracking is essential. The practices should be similar to those adopted to protect buried structures from groundwater; BS 8102:1990 and Coffin *et al.*(1978) give guidance on the design and construction methods for protection of substructures from groundwater.

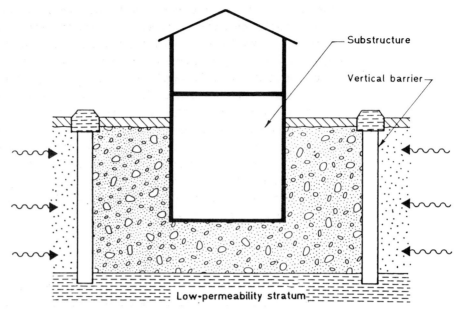

(a) Use of vertical in-ground barriers to prevent lateral gas migration

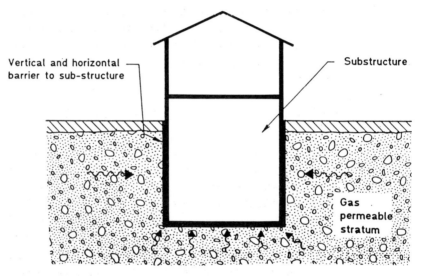

(b) Use of combined vertical and horizontal in-ground barriers

Figure 54 Principle of in-ground barriers to protect subsurface development

In general the specific measures available for gas protection as described in Sections 5 to 8 are also applicable to subsurface development. Excavation and disposal is a technical solution, but is rarely suitable unless the problems of disposal can be solved as discussed in Section 4.3. A more effective solution is the use of in-ground barriers usually in conjunction with in-ground venting techniques (see Sections 6.1 and 6.2). The application of these techniques to subsurface development is discussed below.

12.3.1   In-ground barriers

Vertical barriers may be used to prevent lateral gas migration to subsurface development (see Section 5.1). Regardless of the type or materials used, the barrier should be installed to intercept gas migration from all sides and be deeper than the substructure, constructed either to a level below the groundwater or keyed into a low-permeability stratum as shown in Figure 54. In ground conditions where no low-permeability stratum exists, or if vertical gas migration is also occurring, a horizontal underside barrier might also be required. For the reasons explained in Section 5.1, techniques for providing underside barriers cannot be relied upon to be fully effective. Because of this, it may be better to provide a barrier between the ground and substructure itself. Synthetic liners have been used to provide in-ground horizontal barriers to floors and walls of subsurface development (see Section 5.5). The techniques and methods of applying synthetic barriers are common in civil/building engineering practice to protect subsurface development from the effects of groundwater. BS 8102: 1990 provides guidance on these techniques. Similar techniques and details can be applied to the protection of substructures from gas using low-permeability synthetic barriers. Typical construction details are shown in Figure 55. Indeed most installed synthetic barriers can be designed and selected so as to provide protection to both groundwater and gassing ground.

12.3.2 In-ground venting

For wide-scale protection to general subsurface development the principles of both passive in-ground venting and active in-ground abstraction can be applied. However, as for in-ground barriers, the depth of the venting system will have to be at least the depth of the subsurface development to prevent lateral gas migration beneath the development. As with in-ground barriers, in situations where vertical gas migration occurs, a horizontal gas drainage layer should be installed to prevent accumulation of gases beneath a substructure (see Section 6.1.2). In shallow substructures, e.g. single-storey basements, construction of a passive venting horizontal gas drainage layer connected to a vertical venting trench or trenches would be feasible, as shown in Figure 55.

For deep multi-level substructures this is unlikely to be feasible for the following two reasons:

1. Special excavation techniques, e.g. secant piled or diaphragm walls, are likely to be required to construct a deep substructure. These walls will usually be deeper than the substructure itself such that it becomes impracticable to install a horizontal drainage layer below its floor and connect it to a vertical venting trench or series of gas venting wells beyond the external wall of the structure. Dilution and dispersion can be enhanced by passive venting using vertical vent stacks installed within the substructure itself and taken to inlet and outlet vents located above ground level. However, this will necessitate penetrating the floor which could provide a potential means of ingress into the structure. In addition, the positioning of vent stacks within the structure can provide an additional entry route for gas should it be inadequately sealed at joints or its integrity breached in any way (see Section 2.3).

2. With increasing depth below ground, wind forces and thermal effects creating natural movements of air within a substructure by advection processes will progressively decrease because of the reduction in pressures. Molecular diffusion will probably be the only mechanism by which gas may be dispersed. This will significantly limit the efficacy of venting, particularly where high gas concentrations and emission rates occur (see also Section 6.1.1).

Usually for deep substructures membranes are installed around the internal construction as shown in Figure 56(a) and (b).

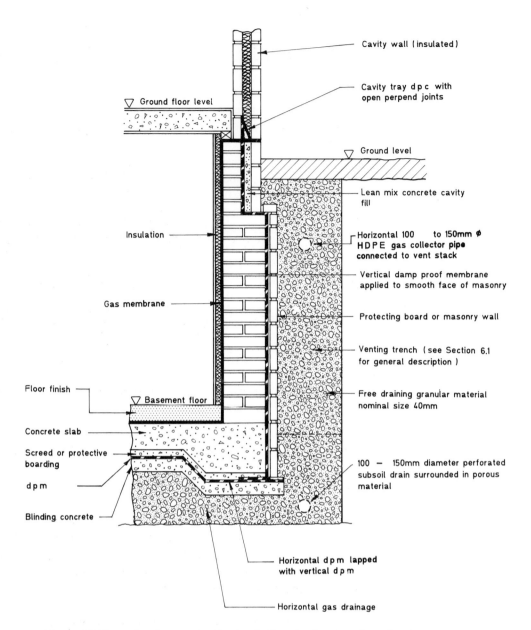

Figure 55 Example of gas protection to shallow depth subsurface development

Active in-ground abstraction can be more effective as a technique to dilute and disperse gas (see also Section 6.2.3). In the UK there are few examples of this to protect subsurface development, but in North America the technique of in-ground venting (known as sub-slab depressurisation) as well as active in-ground venting (known as sub-slab pressurisation) has been used widely to protect subsurface development from hazardous soil gas such as methane and associated gases, VOCs and radon (Clarkin and Brennan, 1991; EPA, 1987 and Samfield, 1992). Figure 57 indicates the principle of these techniques. Box 31 illustrates the use of both active in-ground abstraction and in-ground ventilation applied to subsurface development. Caution should be applied, however, in adopting this principle of introducing air into the ground which when mixed with methane could result in a flammable mixture being created (see also Section 6.1.2).

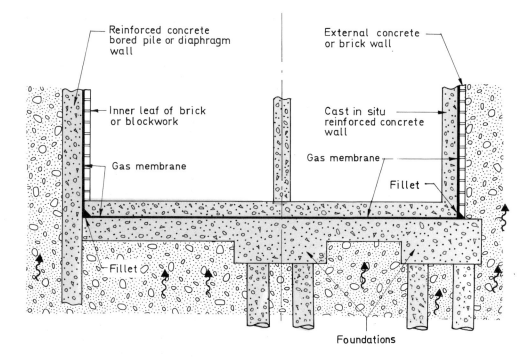

Reinforced concrete
bored pile or diaphragm
wall

External concrete
or brick wall

Inner leaf of brick
or blockwork

Cast in situ
reinforced concrete
wall

Gas membrane

Gas membrane

Fillet

Fillet

Foundations

(a) Membrane installation for
deep bored pile or diaphragm
wall

(b) Membrane installation for deep open excavation

Figure 56 Examples of gas protection measures to deep subsurface development

12.3.3   Internal venting to substructures

In certain situations in-ground barriers or in-ground venting measures cannot be
installed to protect general subsurface development. For example, protection to an
existing basement may not be possible using in-ground techniques, e.g. because of
physical and legal constraints on access. In these circumstances protection measures to
individual substructures will be required.

In addition, the principles of natural ventilation and the method of supplying fresh air
for buildings constructed above ground, as discussed in Section 7.1.2, do not necessarily
hold for subsurface structures.

For shallow substructures partly below ground level, e.g. single-level basements, the
action of wind forces and the resultant pressure distribution cannot be reliably predicted
because of frictional drag effects near the ground surface (i.e. boundary effects). There
is currently no reliable method of quantifying likely air flow rates into such subsurface
structures and thus no reliable method of designing passive venting systems.
Nevertheless, the provision of openings or ducts direct to atmosphere can only promote
ventilation, although quantification of their effect is difficult. General design guidance
for passive venting cable chambers and rooms for telecommunication equipment has
been prepared by the PSA (1977). This recommends the provision, wherever possible,
in the chamber of a low-level inlet for fresh air and a high-level outlet on an appropriate
wall for exhaust air and gas. In this way air circulation within the chamber would
discourage the formation of layers of gas which might have entered from outside, as
shown in Figure 58.

Box 31 Examples of in-ground active abstraction and active venting to subsurface development

In Ontario, Canada, various remedial solutions involving passive in-ground venting at a residential development apparently proved ineffective in controlling methane entry into a basement (CMHC, 1989). The development, comprising some 81 two-storey town houses with full basements, had been constructed in the mid-1970s adjoining a landfill site. At the time of construction of the properties some methane problems were expected because of the nearby landfill. Therefore the developer was required to install in-ground passive venting measures on each housing block and remove any on-site refuse beneath the foundations of the house. The passive in-ground venting system consisted of a 150-mm perforated plastic pipe laid next to the building foundations (below basement level) which was connected to 100-mm diameter risers at the end of each housing block. Despite these mitigative measures high concentrations of methane were recorded. In one housing block there were consistent concentrations of methane above the explosive limit (i.e. 5% methane by volume in air) forcing evacuation of its families. Further remedial measures were attempted based on active in-ground abstraction of gas from the existing in-ground venting system and perimeter collection gas wells. However, these remedial measures also failed to produce a consistent reduction in gas levels. Investigation of installed measures generally indicated that the pipework was poorly fitted and had been partially infilled with silt. A further series of shallow abstraction wells was then installed into the basements of affected house units, and the ground beneath the basement slab pumped both in depressurisation mode (i.e. lower pressure induced beneath basement slab relative to atmospheric resulting in gas abstraction) and pressurisation mode (i.e. higher pressure induced beneath basement slab relative to atmospheric, resulting in active ventilation).

The conclusions of this experiment were that active in-ground abstraction was effective in reducing methane entry into basements. Concentrations of methane were reduced to almost zero levels. A depressurisation (or suction) of some 15 N/m² below atmospheric pressure was sufficient to reduce methane concentrations to less than 15 ppm within the basement.

Active in-ground ventilation by pumping air beneath the basement slabs creating a positive pressure did not prove as effective in reducing methane entry into basements. This was believed to be because of the very low permeability of the soils adjacent to the house reducing the effectiveness of the system to disperse gas.

For substructures constructed entirely below ground level with no direct means of ventilation to atmosphere, passive venting will be ineffective to dilute and disperse gas within a building. Active venting is usually the only means of providing an adequate supply of fresh air to prevent accumulation of dust, odours, vapours, and gases as well as providing humidity and temperature control. Thus the need to provide protection against possible ingress of methane or associated gases from the surrounding ground can usually be accommodated by selecting adequate capacity for the mechanical pumping system and ensuring adequate venting to confined spaces. As discussed in Section 7.2 the majority of active ventilation systems are based on mechanical extraction/natural supply. In some air conditioning systems, however, or where high air quality standards are demanded inside a building, e.g. for computer equipment, active venting systems based on mechanical supply/natural extraction have been applied. In North America and Europe such systems have also been used in residential subsurface development, e.g. house basements, as a simple low-cost protection measure against methane, radon and VOCs (Samfield, 1992 and Connell, 1991). In these systems mechanical fans supply fresh air to the basement. Valves on the vent outlets create a slight positive pressure with respect to atmospheric pressure within the basement. In this way the external gas in the ground is prevented from migrating into the basement through any potential entry point. In the south east of England active venting systems based on mechanical supply/natural extract have also been evaluated by one county council to provide positive ventilation to underfloor void space and substructures of existing residential properties affected by landfill gas. These systems have been developed from those used to overcome the problems of radon gas and provide a positive pressure above atmospheric either within the property or beneath the underfloor void.

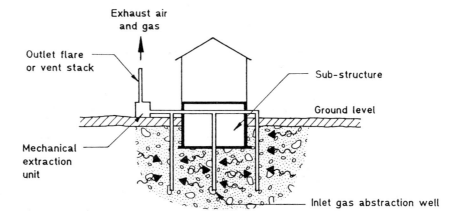

(a) Use of active in-ground abstraction (depressurisation) beneath development

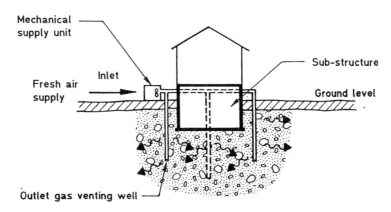

(b) Use of active in-ground venting (pressurisation) measures to protect sub-surface development

Figure 57 Use of active in-ground measures to protect subsurface development

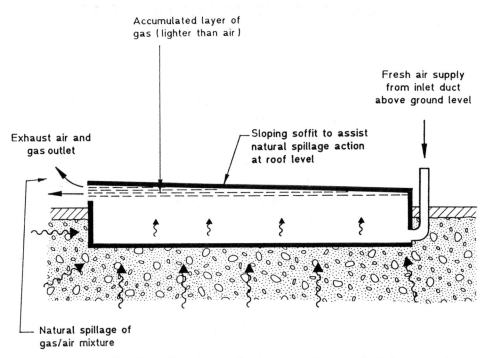

Figure 58   Principle of passive venting to substructures partly below ground
(after PSA, 1977)

13 Long-term management

Long-term management can be defined as the process through which a gas-control system should be operated in order to ensure that:

- required performance standards are identified

- appropriate maintenance and servicing of gas-control systems are identified and planned in order to continue to meet performance standards

- appropriate remedial action is undertaken if performance standards are not achieved.

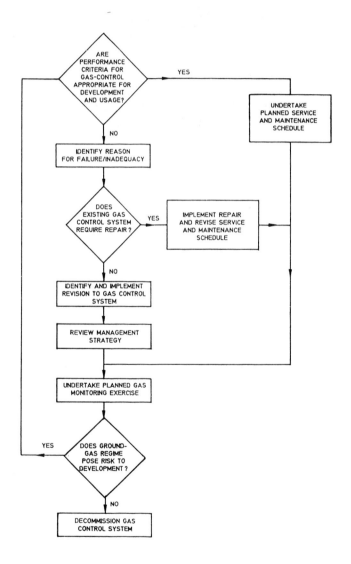

Figure 59 A flow chart for long-term management of gas-control systems

In broad terms, management should apply to all gas-control systems whether they comprise an individual protection measure or a combination of measures. As discussed in Section 10, each gas protection measure has its own limitations and advantages and cannot be certain to be absolutely effective in all situations or circumstances, particularly those which were unknown to, or outside the control of, the designer. Combining a number of protection measures into a gas-control system is a means of reducing the risks of failure. Long-term management provides a framework within which the gas-control system can be operated to meet changes in performance standards and requirements until such time that the hazards from methane and associated gases to a development are removed.

Figure 59 provides a decision flow chart which identifies the elements of management strategy for the installation and operation of a gas-control system. The degree of detail required depends on the protection measures installed and the type of development and use.

Gas-control systems which include active venting and/or gas monitoring and alarm instruments can require detailed management strategy, particularly where they might be integrated with other building services. Decisions have to be considered in relation to their effect on the overall management and operation of a development, e.g. the possible integration of the control of active venting with the normal ventilation and air conditioning requirement within a commercial office or retail development. Examples of such gas-control systems are given in Boxes 16 and 17. Gas-control systems which include a substantial number of mechanical components will require a greater degree of maintenance and servicing to ensure continued efficacy of the systems. In turn this will require a higher level of management than for developments or buildings simply protected by in-ground barriers or passive venting measures. In developments such as commercial offices, retail or public buildings, implementation of a management strategy can be undertaken by an appointed manager and personnel with the necessary skills and equipment to ensure management of the gas-control system is undertaken.

Box 32 Example of long-term management strategy

Crowcroft *et al.* (1991) describe the construction of a motorway service station on the M25 motorway near Thurrock, Essex. The 16-ha site consists of an old quarry which has been infilled with industrial refuse to depths of 20 m which is actively producing landfill gas. Work on the new development commenced in 1988 and consists of an amenity building, motel and refuelling area and parking for some 800 vehicles.

A gas-control system has been installed which consists of:

- an active in-ground abstraction scheme
- a low-permeability horizontal in-ground clay barrier which also incorporates an HDPE membrane (see also Section 5.2)
- a passive venting under-slab void beneath structures
- permanent gas monitoring and alarm equipment installed in under-slab voids and confined spaces to demonstrate the performance of the system.

A long-term management strategy had to be developed in order to ensure that the gas-control system continues to perform adequately. A detailed operational manual was prepared which gave information about the gas-control systems installed and provided instructions to relevant organisations on the regular procedures for servicing, maintenance and procedures in the event of alarm activation. The client and owner of the development retained responsibility for the long-term operation of the gas-control system, but they have retained the services of the design engineer to manage the activities of various contractors working on the site in undertaking the necessary monitoring and maintenance work. The management strategy is kept under review to ensure that appropriate procedures are implemented to meet the changing requirements of either the development or the gas regime.

In contrast, detailed long-term management demanded by sophisticated mechanical/ electrical gas-control systems cannot easily be implemented on residential development.

This is because there is no obvious means by which a management strategy can be implemented except by the owner/occupier of the property. These people will have neither the knowledge nor skills to undertake major service or repair, nor will they necessarily understand the consequences of failing to maintain the system. In these circumstances it is better to devise a gas-control system which requires little or no service or maintenance and can be designed such that it remains effective under worst credible levels of gas regime and environmental conditions. The design of gas-control systems in relation to the type of development is discussed in Section 10. In the case of residential development, difficulties for long-term management are those:

- of gaining access to installed protection measures without disruption to the property and occupants

- ensuring continued long-term management allowing for changes in ownership, etc.

- appointing an agent or body responsible for undertaking long-term management.

Box 33 Example of long-term management for residential development

For a recent residential development constructed on a landfill site, a residents association has been established and is administered by the developer to manage the gas-control system. The duties of the association are to ensure the gas-control system is maintained and serviced in accordance with the designer's instructions and local authority requirements. The duties of the residents association include:

- arranging for periodic gas monitoring from specific monitoring points located in vent stacks set in passive venting trenches and external wall vents connecting under-slab passive venting systems

- regular servicing and maintenance of the gas-control system including prevention of weeds and soil accumulating in passive venting trenches and around external vents to properties

- preventing uncontrolled excavation, lighting of fires, construction of outbuildings and/or building extensions without consent.

These tasks are undertaken in conjunction with other management duties charged to the residents association which included gardening and open landscape maintenance. An annual communal charge is levied on the residents of the development to fund these duties.

Notification that the site is a former landfill site together with a description of the gas–control system that has been installed and the long-term management procedures is passed to each resident on purchasing a property by the developer. All utility companies are informed and have been instructed on procedures to be undertaken when carrying out repairs and maintenance.

The duties of the residents association will continue until such time that the gas-monitoring demonstrates to the satisfaction of the local authority that any risk to the development from the hazards of methane and associated gases has been removed.

For new development long-term management can be implemented by the developer of the site and this can be made a requirement to the granting of planning permission. This can be achieved by an annual communal charge as demonstrated by the case study given in Box 33. Through the planning process conditions can be imposed on the development to control or prohibit any activities which may lead to impairment or failure of the gas-control system. These activities could include:

- uncontrolled excavations

- lighting of bonfires

- uncontrolled building modifications

- erection of temporary buildings or structures including sheds, greenhouses and conservatories.

For existing development, particularly residential, the implementation of long-term management for a gas-control system and appointment of an agent for its implementation cannot be so readily implemented as in the case for new development. In such circumstances the responsibility usually remains with the local authority. A case study describing a scheme operated by a local authority is given in Box 21.

For all long-term management schemes, it is good practice that an operations manual or handbook is produced by the designer/installer of the gas-control system. Irrespective of the scope of the gas-control system the manual should record details of:

- what gas hazards are present and the potential risks
- what gas protection measures have been installed
- how the gas-protection measures operate
- what level of gas monitoring is required
- what procedures have to be followed to maintain and service the protection measures
- what measures are to be taken in the event of failure and/or trigger of an alarm (if fitted)
- how long the management scheme should operate.

Above all an operations manual should be 'user friendly'. For this reason the manual may have to be produced in various levels of detail for the different authorities/interested parties involved. These might include:

- management organisation for gas-control system
- owner of the development/building
- tenant or occupier
- service engineers
- local authority, emergency services, etc.
- utility companies
- Health and Safety Executive.

14 Current capabilities

Most operations that disturb the ground will result in the release of gas or gases of some nature. The key issue is to gain sufficient knowledge of the site history, geography, geology, hydrogeology and the gas regime to formulate an assessment of possible risks to development on or near the ground surface. From this process the need and scope of gas protection measures can be evaluated.

Publicity of tragic accidents such as at Loscoe (Williams and Aitkenhead, 1989) and Abbeystead (HSE, 1985) have heightened awareness in the construction industry of the risks to new and existing development from the hazards of methane and associated gases. Indeed, it is being found that more and more developments have to be designed to take methane into account. In addition, as the findings of this CIRIA project show, many of the case studies are where development has been affected by carbon dioxide as the main component of a gassing source rather than methane. Incidents have occurred where carbon dioxide is produced from natural soils and rocks as well as man-made sources such as landfills.

Government initiative in the UK has been aimed at the control of methane gas at source. Her Majesty's Inspectorate of Pollution (HMIP) wrote to all Waste Disposal Authorities (WDAs) in England and Wales in December 1987 requiring them to identify gassing landfills in their area (HMIP, 1991). The results of this exercise provided the basis for the Supplementary Credit Approval (SCA) scheme which allocated some £150 million, available over a five-year period, to address the problems of gas migration from active and closed landfill sites. The SCA scheme makes resources available to local authorities for works such as investigation and gas control measures at closed landfill sites.

However, similar initiatives to tackle the problems of gas migration from abandoned mine workings or natural gassing sources do not currently exist. The technical difficulties of controlling methane and associated gases from these sources (see Sections 3.3.1 and 4.2), and the financial implications have probably limited this approach as an effective measure for gas protection for development. Advice on the ways in which forward planning of land use and development control can be used to reduce the risks from methane and associated gases is set out in DoE Circulars 21/87 'Development of Contaminated Land' (DoE, 1987) and 17/89 'Landfill Sites: Development Control' (DoE, 1989a), and in guidance from the Interdepartmental Committee on the Redevelopment of Contaminated Land (ICRCL 59/83:1987 and 17/78:1990).

Information gathered for the report reflects a broad range of development affected by methane and associated gases. More than 100 case studies of development affected by these gases have been reviewed and from this information it has been possible to show in broad terms the protection measures adopted in the UK, for characteristic gassing situations whether in terms of methane or carbon dioxide. In broad terms the approach adopted by developers/designers in the UK has been to make development 'gas proof' using specifically designed measures as discussed in this report. The successful design and installation of these protection measures requires thorough understanding and assessment of information at all stages of development including:

- interpretation of ground investigation data, laboratory test results and gas monitoring information

- appraisal of potential future gas generation and choice of parameters to be adopted in the design of gas protection measures

- risk assessment and selection of a gas-control system tailored specifically to building layout and usage

- safety during construction and post development

- consideration of long-term management and monitoring of protection measures to record their efficacy and reliability.

Comprehensive understanding and knowledge of all the above aspects is limited. In general, gas protection systems have been installed into building development more as a precautionary measure rather than on the basis of a quantified risk assessment and technical need. The limited available data regarding the long-term performance of installed protection measures make it difficult to judge or quantify the efficacy of current design procedures. Nevertheless, a measure of success in the design of gas protection measures can be judged perhaps by the limited number of incidents of failure since Loscoe and Abbeystead. Very few incidents have been identified during the preparation of this report where failure of an installed gas-control system or individual protection measure has occurred. Where failure has occurred it can be attributed to the following causes:

- lack of adequate gas monitoring resulting in no appreciation of the presence of gas

- lack of appreciation of ground conditions with the result that no account was taken of differential settlement: this resulted in the rupture and failure of the gas protection measures.

The current capabilities in the UK with regard to protection of new and existing development from methane and associated gases in the ground are summarised in Table 31. Although there is still much to be learnt about the quantitative design of gas protection measures, many of the requirements for their satisfactory performance can be based on good engineering practice. Failures are rare, which suggests that gas protection measures adopted by practitioners and designers in development are generally successful.

Table 31 Summary of current capabillities

Aspect	Capability			Remarks
	Poor	Satisfactory	Good	
Identification of problem			✓	Good knowledge of likely sources and ground conditions.
Assessment of gas monitoring information	✓			Usually inadequate period of gas monitoring particularly the need to measure and evaluate gas emission rates.
Assessment of need for gas protection measures		✓		Use of the Building Regulations (DoE, 1992) and WMP 27 (DoE, 1991); but little understanding of risk assessment.
Design and installation of gas protection measures:				
• basic requirements	✓			Could be improved by careful workmanship and installation techniques on site.
• excavation and removal at source	✓			Not usually appropriate.
• in-ground barriers		✓		Little knowledge of permeability of materials to gas and long-term performances.
• passive in-ground venting		✓		Limited knowledge of principles.
• active in-ground venting		✓		Effectiveness influenced by site conditions.
• passive venting beneath structures	✓			Limited knowledge of quantitative design.
• active venting beneath structures		✓		Experience from heating and ventilation engineering principles.
• membranes			✓	Usually well designed and installed.
Gas monitoring post construction		✓		Tendency to rely on gas monitoring as a protection measure and a substitute for adequate gas monitoring during site investigation. Limited knowledge of gas behaviour in buildings.
Long-term management	✓			Tend to build 'belt and braces' to avoid long-term management.
Record performance of protection measures	✓			Limited undertaking in most development projects except where active venting measures are installed.

References

ASHTON, S.H. (1991)
Landfill gas – The elusive menace
Proc. Symp. on methane – facing the problems
Paper 3.2, Nottingham, March

BAKER, W. (1987)
Investigation Strategy
City of Birmingham Development Department Symposium on Methane Generating Sites
Industrial Research Laboratories, Birmingham, 9 December

BARRY, D.L. (1986)
Hazards from methane (and carbon dioxide)
In : *Reclaiming contaminated land* (Cairney, T. ed.)
Blackie, Glasgow

BARRY, D.L. (1987)
Hazards from methane on contaminated sites
In : *Building on marginal and derelict land*
Thomas Telford, London

BARRY, D.L. and RAYBOULD, J.G. (1988)
Landfill gas migration hazards
Proc. 2nd International Conference on construction in areas of abandoned mineworkings, Mineworkings '88
Edinburgh

BARRY, D., STEEDS, J. and SHEPHERD, M. (In preparation)
A guide to safe working practices for contaminated sites
to be issued as CIRIA Funders Report CP/FR/8 prior to open publication

BATH, A.H., DARLING, W.G., HITCHMAN, S.P., ANDREWS, J.N., CAVE, M.R., GREEN, K.A. and REDDER, S. (1988)
Chemical and stable isotope analyses of dissolved gases and groundwater seepages collected from Wyresdale Tunnel
Tech. Rep. Brit. Geol. Surv.
Fluid Processes Group WE/88/1C, Keyworth, Nottingham, November 1987

BAVER, L.D., GARDNER, W.H. and GARDNER, W.R. (1972)
Soil Physics 4th edition
John Wiley and Sons, New York

BELL, F.G. (1981)
Foundation engineering in difficult ground
Butterworth & Co., London,

BERESFORD, J.J. (1989)
Permanent works design
Proc. symp. on methane –facing the problems
Paper 4.3, Nottingham, September

BRITISH GAS (1990)
Gas in housing – a technical guide
The British Gas Housing Development Departments
British Gas Plc

BSI (BRITISH STANDARDS INSTITUTION)

BS 1377:1975	*Methods of test for soils for civil engineering purposes (superseded by BS 377:1990)*
BS 5345:1976	*Code of practice for selection, installation and maintenance of electrical apparatus for use in potentially explosive atmospheres*
BS 5501:1977	*Electrical apparatus for potentially explosive atmospheres; Part 1 general requirements*
BS 5588:1991	*Fire precautions in the design, construction and use of buildings*
BS 5720:1979	*Code of practice for mechanical ventilation and air conditioning in buildings*
BS 5925:1991	*Code of practice for ventilation principles and designing for natural ventilation*
BS 6020:1981	*Instruments for the detection of combustible gases : Specification for general requirements and test methods*
BS 6164:1990	*Code of practice for safety in tunnelling in the construction industry*
BS 8102 :1990	*Code of practice for protection of structures against water from the ground*
BS 8110:1985	*Structural use of concrete : Part 1. Code of practice for design and construction*
BS 8207:1985	*Code of practice for energy efficiency in buildings*
BS 8301:1985	*Code of practice for building drainage*
CP3:1972	*Code of basic data for the design of buildings; Section V : Part 2. Wind loads*

BRE (1977)
Digest 206:*Ventilation requirements*
Building Research Establishment

BRE (1978)
Digest 210 : *Principles of natural ventilation*
Building Research Establishment

BRE (1982)
Digest 141 : *Wind environment around tall buildings*
Building Research Establishment

BRE (1989)
Digest 346 : *The assessment of wind loads*
Part 1 : Background and method
Building Research Establishment, July

BRE (1989)
Digest 346 : *The assessment of wind loads*
Part 2 : Classification of structures
Building Research Establishment, August

BRE (1989)
Digest 346 : *The assessment of wind loads*
Part 3 : Wind climate in the United Kingdom
Building Research Establishment, August

BRE (1989)
Digest 346 : *The assessment of wind loads*
Part 4 : Terrain and building factors and gust peak features
Building Research Establishment, August

BRE (1989)
Digest 346 : *The assessment of wind loads*
Part 5 : The assessment of wind speed over topography
Building Research Establishment, November

BRE (1989)
Digest 346 : *The assessment of wind loads*
Part 6 : Loading coefficients for typical buildings
Building Research Establishment, November

BRE (1990)
Digest 346 : *The assessment of wind loads*
Part 7 : Wind speeds for serviceability and fatigue assessments
Building Research Establishment

BRE (1990)
Digest 346 : *The assessment of wind loads*
Part 8 : Internal pressures
Building Research Establishment, December

BRE (1991a)
Digest 364 : Design of timber floors to prevent decay
Building Research Establishment, August

BRE (1991b)
Digest 365 : *Design of soakaways*
Building Research Establishment, September

BRE (1991c)
Construction of new buildings on gas – contaminated land
Building Research Establishment Report

BUSWELL, A.M. and LARSON, T.E. (1937)
Methane in groundwaters
J. Amer. Waterworks Assn, Vol. 29, pp. 1978 –82

CAMPBELL, D.J.V. (1987)
Landfill gas migration – monitoring and controls
United Kingdom Atomic Energy Authority, Harwell, March

CMHC (1989)
Kitchener townhouse study of soil gas ventilation as a remedial measure for methane entry into basements
Prepared for the Canada Mortgage and Housing Corporation by CH2M Hill Engineering Ltd

CARD, G.B. (1981)
The properties and performance of bentonite cement slurries for use as hydraulic cut-offs
PhD Thesis, King's College, University of London, April

CARD, G.B. and ROCHE, D.P. (1991)
The design of gas control measures for development affected by landfill gas
Proc. symp. on methane – facing the problems
Paper 3.3, Nottingham, March

CARDEN, S.G., GOODWIN, P.J. and THOMPSON, P.G. (1983)
A problem of surface methane emission
Municipal Engineer, Vol. 110, no. 4, pp. 133-43, April

CARPENTER, R.J. (1988)
Building redevelopment on disused landfill sites – overcoming the landfill gas problem?
Proc. ISWA (International Solid Wastes Association) 88
ISWA Conference, Copenhagen, Denmark

CARPENTER, R.J., GOAMAN, H.F., LOWE, G.W. and PECKSEN, G.N. (1985)
Guidelines for site investigations of contaminated land
GLC Scientific Services Branch, *London Environmental Supplement,* No. 12

CHERENKO, F.A. (1974)
Bedford's basic principles of ventilation and heating
H.K. Lewis and Co. Ltd

CHILDS, K.A. (1985)
In-ground barriers and hydraulic measures, pp. 145–82
In : *Contaminated land – Reclamation and treatment* (Smith, M.A. ed.)
Plenum Press, New York, 1985

CHIPP, J.P. (1990)
Geotechnical processes for the prevention and control of pollution
Symp. on management and control of waste fill sites
Leamington Spa

CIBSE (1986)
Air infiltration and natural ventilation, Volume A4
The Chartered Institution of Building Services Engineers, London

CLARK, A.D., BOARD, N.P. and GRIFFITHS, C.M. (1991)
Protection of structures from landfill gas
Proc. symp. on methane – facing the problems,
Paper 5.4, Nottingham, March

CLARKIN, M. and BRENNAN, T. (1991)
Radon-resistant construction techniques for new residential construction : Technical guidance
Air and Energy Engineering Research Laboratory
US Environmental Protection Agency
E.P.A/625/2-91/032, February

CLOW, D.G. (1991)
Protection against the gas hazard – the evolution of a policy in British Telecom
Proc. symp. on methane – facing the problems
Paper 4.2, Nottingham, March

COFFIN, F.G ., BECKMANN, P. and PEARCE, T. (1978)
Guide to the design of waterproof basements
CIRIA Guide 5

CONNELL, J.J. (1991)
Radon in buildings
Environmental Research Unit, Dublin, Republic of Ireland

COUTH, R.J. (1990)
Liverpool International Garden Festival Site – A case study
Hazardous gases in the environment – A seminar.
Institute of Geologists, North West Group, April

CREEDY, D.P. (1989)
Geological sources of methane in relation to surface and underground hazards
Proc. symp. on methane-facing the problems
Paper 1.4, Nottingham, September

CREEDY, D.P. (1990)
Hazardous gases in the environment
Seminar. Institute of Geologists, North West Group, April

CREEDY, D.P.(1991)
An introduction to the geological aspects of methane occurrence and control in British
deep coal mines
Qtly J.Eng. Geol., Vol. 24, pp. 209 –20

CROWCROFT, P., MORRISON, I. and HOLDEN, F. (1991)
The design and commissioning of a gas control system – Thurrock M25 motorway
services area
Proc. symp. on methane – facing the problems
Paper 3.4, Nottingham, March

CROWHURST, D. (1987)
Measurement of gas emissions from contaminated land
Building Research Establishment Report BR 100

CROWHURST, D. and MANCHESTER, S.J. (1993)
The measurement of methane and associated gases from the ground
CIRIA Report 131, CIRIA, London 1993

CSS (1987)
Coping with landfill gas
County Surveyors Society Report No 4/4, May

D'APPOLONIA, D.J. (1980)
Soil-bentonite slurry trench cut-offs
J. Geotech. Eng. Div. ASCE, Vol. 106, GT4, pp. 399 – 417

DARLING, W.G. (1981)
The analysis of free and dissolved gases by chromatography
Tech. Rep. Brit. Geol. Surv.
Hydrogeology Series WD/ST/81, 48pp

DARLING, W.G. (1985)
Methane in the chalk groundwater of central London
Tech. Rep. Brit. Geol. Surv.
Hydrogeology Series WD/ST/85/3

DARLING, W.G. and BATH, A.H. (1986)
Methane concentrations in some Scottish hydroelectric tunnels
Tech. Rep. Brit. Geol. Surv.
Hydrogeology Series WD/ST/86/7

DEACON, R.C. (1987)
Concrete ground floors : their design, construction and finish
Wexham Springs, Cement and Concrete Association, 1987 Publication 48.034

DoE (1986)
Landfilling Wastes : a technical memorandum for the disposal of wastes on landfill sites, Waste Management Paper No. 26.
Department of the Environment
HMSO, London

DoE (1987)
Planning Circular 21/87
Development of contaminated land
HMSO, London

DoE (1989a)
Planning Circular 17/89 (Circular 38/89: Welsh Office)
Landfill sites : development control
HMSO, London

DoE (1989b)
Hazardous Gas Research Study. *Gas protection measures for buildings*
Report for the Department of the Environment by Ove Arup and Partners

DoE (1991)
Waste Management Paper No: 27. *The control of landfill gas*, 2nd edition
Department of the Environment, Wastes Technical Division
HMSO, London.

DoE (1992)
The Building Regulations Approved Document
Department of the Environment
HMSO, London

DTp (1991)
Manual of contract documents for highway works
Volume 1, Specification for highway works
Department of Transport, December, HMSO, London

DORE, E. (1983)
Suspended concrete ground floors for houses
Cement and Concrete Association Publication 48.051

DORLING, T.A. (1978)
Activated carbon in odour control
Report No : LR 293 (AP) July 1978 (reprinted 1988)
Warren Spring Laboratory, Stevenage

DOWNIE, A.R. and TREHARNE,G. (1979)
Dynamic consolidation of refuse at Cwmbran
Symposium on the Engineering behaviour of industrial and urban fill,
Midland Geotechnical Society at Birmingham University, April

DUTTON, C., GAHIR, J.S. and JONES, H.L.M. (1991)
Landfill gas – experience in the Black Country
Proc. symp. on methane – facing the problems
Paper 6.1, Nottingham, March

EDWARDS, J. (1989)
Gases – Their basic properties
Proc. symp. on methane-facing the problems
Paper 1.3, Nottingham, September

EPA (1987)
Removal of radon from household water
United States : Environmental Protection Agency. Washington DC 20460
Research and Development. OPA-87-011, September

FIRST, M.W., VILES, F.J. and LEVIN, S. (1986)
Control of toxic and explosive hazards in buildings erected on landfills
Public Health Report, Vol. 81: No. 5 pp. 419 –28, May

FREEZE, R.A. and CHERRY, J.A. (1979)
Groundwater
Prentice-Hall, Englewood Cliffs, New Jersey

FUGLER, D. (1992)
Study of houses affected by hazardous lands
Prepared for Canada Mortgage and Housing Corporation by CH2M Hill Engineering
Ltd

FUNG, R. (1980)
Protective barriers for containment of toxic materials
Pollution Technology Review No. 66
Noyes Data Corporation, 1980

GIROUD, J.P. and BONAPARTE, R. (1990)
Leakage through liners constructed with geomembranes
Part 1 Geotextiles and Geomembranes, Vol. 8, No. 1, pp. 27 – 62, 1990

GOLDMAN, L.J., KINGSBURY, G.L., NORTHERM, C.M. and TRUESDALE, R.S.
(1986)
Design, construction, maintenance and evaluation of clay liners for hazardous waste
facilities
United States : Environmental Protection Agency
Research Triangle Institute, EPA/68-03-3149-1-2

GORDON, D.L., LORD, J.A. and TWINE, D. (1987)
The Stockley Park Project
In : *Building on marginal and derelict land*
Thomas Telford, London

GREENWOOD, D. and THOMSON, G.H. (1984)
Ground stabilisation : deep compaction and grouting
ICE Works Construction Guides
Thomas Telford, London

HARRIES, C.R., SLEAT, R., SEVILLE, T., HAROLD, P. and WALDOCK, J. (1990)
Inhibition of methanogenesis in anaerobically decomposing municipal solid waste
Final report to the Department of the Environment, March

HARRIES, C.R., WITHERINGTON, P.J. and McENTEE, J.M. (1995)
The interpretation of subsurface gas measurements
Report 151, CIRIA, London

HARRISON, R.M. (1990)
Pollution : causes, effects and control, 2nd Edition
Royal Society of Chemistry, Cambridge

HARTLESS, R. (1992)
Methane and associated hazards : a bibliography
CIRIA Special Publication 79. CIRIA, London

HASSE, H.J. and HITZE, R. (1986)
All round encapsulation of hazardous wastes by means of injection gels and cut-off
materials resistant to aggressive agents
ESME3 *Seminar on Hazardous Waste,* Bergoumo, Italy, 1986

HAXO, H.E. (1975)
Assessing synthetic and admixed materials for lining landfills
In : *Proceedings of gas and leachate from landfills : formulation, collection and
treatment symposium.*
U.S. Environmental Protection Agency, Rutgers University,
EPA 600/9-76 004. pp 130–158, March 1975.

HMIP (1991)
*Landfill gas : a report of the findings of surveys carried out by HM Inspectorate of
Pollution to assess the scale of the problem and provide recommendations for further
action*
Her Majesty's Inspectorate of Pollution, April

HSE (Health and Safety Executive) (1985)
*The Abbeystead explosion – A report of the investigation by the Health and Safety
Executive into the explosion on 23 May 1984 at the valve house of the Lune/Wyre water
transfer scheme at Abbeystead*
HMSO, London

HSE (1991)
Protection of workers and the general public during development of contaminated land
HMSO, London

HSE (1992)
EH40/92 Occupational exposure limits 1992
HMSO, London

HOLTZ, R.D., JAMIOLKOWSKI, M.B., LANCELLOTA, R. and PEDRONI, R. (1991)
Prefabricated vertical drains : design and performance
CIRIA Book 11
CIRIA, London and Butterworth-Heinemann, Oxford

HOLZMANN, P. (1991)
Innovative glass technology for rubbish dump sealing walls : by the example of a vertical glass sealing wall
Flachglas Consult GMBH / Philip Holzmann AG
Pilkington Translation Dept PJA / dmf Register No. R+D 90
Issued 1, March, File No. 10899

HOOKER P.J. and BANNON, M.P. (1993)
Methane : its occurrence and hazards in construction
Report 130, CIRIA, London

INGLE, J.A. and KAVANAGH, S.T. (1991)
Case studies of the use of slurry walls to control leachate and gas migration
Proc. symp. on methane – facing the problems
Paper 3.1, Nottingham, March

ICRCL (1987)
Guidance Note 59/83, Guidance on the assessment and redevelopment of contaminated land
Interdepartmental Committee on the Redevelopment of Contaminated Land
DoE, 2nd edition, July

ICRCL (1990)
Guidance Note 17/78, Notes on the development and after use of landfill sites
Interdepartmental Committee on the Redevelopment of Contaminated Land
DoE, 8th edition, December

JAITLY, P.K. (1987)
Methane contamination – Synopsis of current information and practice
Docklands Joint Committee : Working group on methane, 1987
Department of Architecture and Civic Design
Greater London Council

JEFFERIS, S.A. (1972)
The composition and uses of slurries in civil engineering practice
PhdD Thesis, King's College, University of London

JEFFERIS, S.A. (1990)
Bentonite-cement cut-off walls for waste containment from specification to *insitu* performance
Symposium on management and control of waste fill sites, Leamington Spa

JEFFERIS, S.A. (1991)
Containment : cut-off walls
In : *Short course on contaminated land*
European Centre for Pollution Research, Queen Mary and Westfield College, University
of London, September

JOHNSON, B. (1986)
Methane gas seeps into Seattle community homes
Management World Wastes, Vol. 29, Part 13, pp. 8–12

KANOL, D.W. and ZETHER, G.H. (1990)
Proceedings of the 5th sewage and refuse symposium,
Abwassertechnische Vereinnigung ev., Munich, pp. 859–70

KRAUSE, R. (1989)
The use of high density polyethylene membranes for methane containment
Proc. symp. on methane – facing the problems
Paper 3.2, Nottingham, September

LEACH, S.J and BLOOMFIELD, D.P. (1974)
Ventilation in relation to toxic and flammable gases in buildings
Building Research Establishment Current Paper CP 36/74, February

LEACH, B.A. and GOODGER, H.K. (1991)
Building on derelict land
CIRIA Special publication 78-PSA Civil Engineering Technical Guide 60

MANLEY, B.J.W., TILLOTSON, H.S., TIPPING, R.H. and GARDNER, N. (1991)
An innovative approach to the retrofitting of building protection measures to
developments on landfill sites
Proc. symp. on methane–facing the problems
Paper 5.1, Nottingham, March

MITCHELL, J.K. (1976)
Fundamentals of soil behaviour
John Wiley and Sons, New York

NCB (1979)
Ventilation in coal mines – a handbook for colliery ventilation officers
National Coal Board
NFPA (1988)
Venting of deflagrations
National Fire Protection Association, NFPA 68

NJUG (1979)
Provision of mains and services by public utilities on residential estates
Publication No. 2, National Joint Utilities Group, November

NJUG (1983)
*Model guidelines for the planning and installation of utilities supplies to new building
developments*
Publication No. 5, May

NJUG (1984)
Service entries for new dwellings on residential estates
Publication No. 6, September

NJUG (1986)
Recommended positioning of utilities mains and plant for new works
Publication No. 7, December

NRA (1991)
Policy and practice for the protection of groundwater : draft for consultation
National Rivers Authority, November

NWWDO (1988)
Guidelines on the use of landfill liners
North West Waste Disposal Officers landfill Liners Sub-Group
Lancashire Waste Disposal Authority, October

O'RIORDAN, N.J. and MILLOY, C.J. (1994)
Risk assessment for methane and other gases for the ground
Report 152, CIRIA, London

O'RIORDAN, N. and WARREN, R. (1991)
Methane and the design of foundation systems
Proc. symp. on methane – facing the problems
Paper 5.2, Nottingham, March

ORR,W.E., WOOD, A.M., BEAVER, J.J., IRELAND, R.J. and BEAGLEY, D.P.
(1991)
Abbeystead outfall works : background to repairs and modifications and lessons learnt
J. Inst. Water. Env. Man, Vol. 5 February, pp. 7–20

OSCROFT, G. (1992)
An explosive problem
Surveyor, 6 February, pp. 15

OWEIS, I.S. and KHERA, R.P. (1990)
Geotechnology of waste management
Butterworth & Co. London,

PARKER, A. (1986)
Landfill gas – a potential environmental hazard
Disasters, Vol. 10, No. 1, 65-9
PARKINSON, C.D. (1991)
The permeability of landfill liners to leachate,
In *: The planning and engineering of landfills*, Midlands Geotechnical Society,
Birmingham

PECKSEN, G.N. (1986)
Methane and the development of derelict land
London Environmental Supplement, Summer 1985, No. 13
London Scientific Services, Land Pollution Group

PEGG, I.D. (1990)
Detection and investigation of leaks in geomembrane liners
Geosynthetics World, Vol. 1, No. 2, pp. 7 – 14

PSA (1977)
The protection of operational buildings from gas
Property Services Agency Report No. TAD (77)1,
PSA, Directorate of Post Office, Croydon

QUAY, P.D., STAGG, L.K., LANSDOWN, J.M. and WILBUR, D.O. (1988)
Isotopic composition of methane released from wetlands : implications for the increase
in atmospheric methane
Global biogeochemical cycles, Vol. 2, pp. 385–98

RAYBOULD, J.G. and ANDERSON, D.J. (1987)
Migration of landfill gas and its control by grouting – a case history
Qtly J. Eng. Geol., Vol. 20, No. 1, pp. 75 – 84

ROBINSON, N. and GRAYSON, R. (1990)
Natural methane seepages in the Lancashire coalfield
Land and Mineral Surveyor, July

ROCHE, D.P. and CARD, G.B. (1991)
Gas-control measures for development of land affected by landfill gas
In : *Land reclamation : an end to dereliction?* (Davies, M.C.R. ed.)
pp.125–130
Elsevier Science Publishers, London

RAYBOULD, J.G., ROWAN, S.P. and BARRY, D.L. (1993)
Methane investigation strategies
Report 150, CIRIA, London

RYS, L.J. and JOHNS, A.F. (1985)
The investigation and development of a landfill site
In : *Proc. 1st Int. TNO Conf. on contaminated soil, Utrecht,*
(Assink, J.W. and Van de Brink, W.J. eds.) pp. 625–36, November

SAMFIELD, M.M. (1992)
Soil-gas transport of organic chemicals into building structures : A literature review.
Radon Mitigation Branch, Air and Energy Engineering Research Laboratory, US
Environmental Protection Agency, March

SHERIFF, J.A., STEVENSON, D.A. and WRIGHT, P.A. (1991)
From site survey to building design – the safe, cost effective solution
Proc. symp. on methane – facing the problems,
Paper 4.4, Nottingham, March

STAFF, M.G. and SCEAL, J.S. (1992)
Methane and associated hazards to construction research and information needs
CIRIA Project Report 5, CIRIA, London, 1992

STAFF, M.G., SIZER, K.E. and NEWSON, S.R. (1991)
The potential for surface emissions of methane from abandoned mine workings.
Proc. symp. on methane – facing the problems
Paper 1.1, Nottingham, March

STEARNS, R.P. and PETOYAN, G.S. (1984)
Waste Management Research, Vol. 2, pp. 75–83

SWAIN, F.M. (1986)
Composition of marsh gases in the central and eastern United States
Applied Geochemistry, Vol. 1. pp. 301–305

THOMSON J.R. (1987)
Engineering safety assessment
Longman

TONKYN, C. (1989)
Detection and measurement
Proc. symp. on methane – facing the problems
Paper 2.2, Nottingham, September

WRc (1990)
Effects of soil contaminants on materials used for distribution of water
Water Research Council Report ECI 9168, Swindon

WATERS, T.C. (1960)
Reinforced concrete as a material for containment
Proc. of symp. on nuclear reactor containment buildings and pressure vessels
pp. 50-60
Butterworths, London

WHEELER, S.J., SHAM, W.K. and THOMAS, S.D. (1989)
Gas pressures in unsaturated off-shore soils
Canadian Geotechnical Journal, October

WILLIAMS, G.M. and AITKENHEAD, N. (1989)
The gas explosion at Loscoe, Derbyshire
Proc. symp on methane – facing the problems,
Paper 3.6, Nottingham, September

WILLIAMS, G.M. and HITCHMAN, S.P. (1989)
The generation and migration of gases in the subsurface
Proc. symp. on methane – facing the problems
Paper 2.1, Nottingham, September

YOUNG, O.C. and O'REILLY, M.P. (1983)
A guide to design loadings for buried rigid pipes
Transport and Road Research Laboratory, DTp
HMSO, London

YOUNG, P. and PARKER, A. (1984)
Vapours, odours and toxic gases from landfills
Industrial waste management and testing : Third symposium
ASTM STP 851 (Jackson, L.P., Rohlik, A.R. and Conway, R.A. eds) ASTM,
Philadelphia, PA, pp. 24–41